TURKISH STORIES

TURKISH STORIES

Fuad Kavur

ISBN 978-1-7397835-0-1

Cover photo by Elmar Ludwig.

Printed and bound in Great Britain by Clays Ltd, Elcograf S.p.A.

Typeset using Atomik ePublisher from Easypress Technologies.

www.curzonbooks.com

CONTENTS

A SUNDAY OUTING

The Hurlingham is one of the most exclusive clubs in London. But what makes it special is, on the outskirts of London, boasting of numerous tennis courts and golf courses – it is more like an exclusive Californian club! Also, admitting ladies and children, The Hurlingham is the ideal place for a family outing.

Of course, in June 1963, on my second day in England, in my mid-teens, I was hardly familiar with these facts. All I remember, it was a warm Sunday, and my uncle, with whom I was staying, announced,

'We can't stay in on such a lovely day, let's go out!'

My uncle, my father's elder brother, was the Turkish Ambassador to London. After having served five years as ambassador to Nikita Khrushchev's Moscow, he was recently appointed to the Court of St James's, a posting which he regarded as his reward for many years of hardship, at the height of the Cold War, in the Soviet Union.

The ambassador's residence in London, a palatial building, was in Portland Place where uncle lived with his wife and son, his only child.

My cousin – the same age as me – was born in Helsinki during my uncle's first ambassadorial posting. Thereafter, the boy tagged along wherever his father was posted: Sofia, Tokyo and Moscow, which meant he never learnt much Turkish. Whereas, he spoke fluent German, due to his German Nanny; French, because of his schooling at French Lycées wherever his father was posted; Russian, due to having spent five years in Moscow; and last but not least, English, which he picked up in no time due to staying in England – greatly helped by his obvious aptitude for languages.

That, alas, was more than one could say about my uncle. Sadly, for one serving as an ambassador to London, his English left something to be desired. In all fairness, when uncle started his career, in the early 1930s, the Lingua Franca was still French, which he spoke like a native.

Indeed, before attending Heidelberg to study International Law, uncle was educated at the famous Lycée Galatasaray in Istanbul, where, in 1920s, all teaching was carried out in French – by native tutors. The school was modelled on Lycée Condorcet or Eton College – where boys wore top hats and tails, and they were groomed for the Turkish civil service – especially the diplomatic.

Mind you, not only did uncle speak French fluently, but he was also well versed in its literature. Often at dinner, after the odd glass of Raki or two, he would break into verse, reciting from French romantics – Victor Hugo, Gérard de Nerval or Alfred de Musset. But his favourite was Alfred de Vigny. So, before the evening was out, we would invariably be treated to a rendition of 'La Mort du Loup'.

Gémir, pleurer, prier, est également lâche,
Fais énergiquement ta longue et lourde tâche,
Dans la voie où le sort a voulu t'appeler,
Puis, après, come moi, souffre et meurs sans parler.

However, uncle was not all sentiment either. If he wanted, he could be as tough as old boots. Maybe this was due to the fact, his first posting, as a Head of Legation, had been Berlin – where he served as Chargé d'Affaires to Adolf Hitler's Germany.

On many evenings, we were treated to his retrospective retelling of meetings with Joachim von Ribbentrop or the Führer.

On one occasion, an irate Hitler had told my uncle that if he wanted to, he could have invaded Turkey within days. Undaunted, uncle simply reminded him that in Austria, parents still cautioned their wayward children with: 'Benehme dich, sonst kommt die Türken!'[1]

Then, with a generous gulp of Raki, uncle would proudly conclude his story: 'Hitler advanced as far as the Greek islands, but… he knew where to draw the line.'

On other occasions, we were treated to uncle's reminiscences about Nikita Khrushchev's Moscow. The names of the Soviet Nomenklatura – Molotov, Gromyko, Mikoyan, Voroshilov conjured for me the mysterious, and somewhat alarming world of communism.

So, now, after five years in the Soviet Union, uncle was delighted, to be finally appointed ambassador plenipotentiary to the Court of St James's. Mind you, London did suit him best. He always had been an 'Old School' diplomat, and he did enjoy playing the part.

His suits were tailored at Saville Row; his shirts were made at Turnbull & Asser; and shoes hand made at Cobbs. Even the accessories were selected with care. His pig-skin wallet, which he used to call his 'porte-feuilles', was acquired at Swaine & Adeney at St James's, as was his briefcase. In short, uncle was definitely in his element in London, and enjoyed every minute of it. Or, so it seemed until that fateful Sunday.

---

1 Behave yourself, or Turks will come and get you!

At the time, there was another visitor staying at the ambassadorial residence at Portland Place – a famous Turkish violinist, Ayla Erduran. In her late twenties, she was a most attractive and sensuous blond. With her long, harvest-gold hair running down to her waist, her slender figure, her huge green eyes and sexy mouth, she looked the spitting image of a French movie star of the time – Brigitte Bardot.

Few years previously, when Ayla was studying with the great Soviet violinist David Oistrakh, she had stayed at the Moscow embassy, and that is how she and my uncle got to know each other. Now in London, Ayla was to give a concert at the Festival Hall, the Bach double concerto, with Yehudi Menuhin.

So, our Sunday outing started with the ambassadorial Mercedes, driven by the Portuguese driver, Enriquez, setting out from Portland Place.

My uncle and his wife, an affected woman who looked just like Mrs Wallis Simpson – the American wife of Edward VIII, took the back seat of the car. Seated next to her was the Brigitte Bardot look-alike violinist; with my uncle next to her. My cousin and I were in the front, next to Enriquez, the Portuguese driver. Uncle spoke:

'The Hurlingham, Enriquez.'

'Muj Bien, Excellenz.'

On that note, the Portuguese driver started the car, and we were off. Given this was my first day in England, as we drove along, I was treated to an Ambassadorial commentary about sights of interest:

'On your left, the BBC; Piccadilly Circus; Trafalgar Square; Nelson's Column…'

As we reached Whitehall, uncle's tone became more serious: 'Downing Street – the British Prime Minister's home.' Then, as we passed a sumptuous edifice in Whitehall, uncle spoke:

'The *Foreyn* Office!'

In his voice, I could hear the professional admiration:

'From that building the British Empire was ruled.'

As we drove further along, uncle made a fleeting reference to a gothic edifice on our left,

'The Houses of Parliament.'

Thereafter, the running commentary died down, and uncle contained himself flirting diplomatically with the sexy violinist:

'My dear, is your Stradivarius properly insured?'

My cousin and I, eavesdropping from the front seat or car, remained silent. It was obvious, uncle had a soft spot for the Brigitte Bardot look-alike.

However, our trip was not destined to run smoothly. The first signs of trouble appeared as we picked up the motorway – which, due to a huge advertisement in neon lights, 'Lucozade', I recognised to be the same as the one when I was fetched from the airport, the day before.

Now, having left central London behind, we were speeding along the motorway, and I could see signposts pointing to Heathrow airport.

It was at that point, I noticed, my cousin exhibiting symptoms of unease.

'Shall I open the window?' I whispered. There was no answer.

In the meantime, my uncle's wife was busy telling the sexy violinist, how much she adored classical music, and had even, considered becoming a concert pianist herself…

By now, Enriquez, the Portuguese driver, had put his foot down and we were cruising along the M4 at a neat 70 mph. Suddenly, all conversation, pretentious or otherwise had dried up, and a pregnant silence reigned in the car.

By now, however, my cousin's unease became more noticeable. Curiously, I noticed similar signs with Enriquez – the Portuguese driver. Finally, my cousin whispered to me,

'We left the club miles behind.' I whispered back:

'Tell the driver.'

My cousin gave me a look as if to say 'Don't be so stupid!' By now, the signs on the motorway pointed towards a place called Windsor. Finally, my cousin took a deep breath and broke the news.

'We passed the club miles ago.' My uncle replied:

'We're nowhere near it yet.'

But my cousin, who had a scientific mind, dug his heels in.

'The turning for The Hurlingham was by the Hammersmith flyover.' My uncle replied,

'Warum schweigst-du nicht? Ausserdem, Enriquez ist der fahrer.'[1]

I later learnt, when uncle wanted to deliver a serious message to his son, he always chose German. My cousin, equally adamant, replied – also in German:

'Es ist mir wurst. Aber, bald, treffen wir in Oxford ein!'[2]

Now, to reassure himself, uncle casually asked Enriquez,

'Will we be at the club soon?'

Although, by then, he too had realised all was not well; I assume out of fear, Enriquez replied:

'Si, Exzellenz.'

'Siehst-du?'[3] Uncle retorted, to his disrespectful son.

---

1   Why don't you shut up? Besides, Enriquez is the driver.

2   I don't care. But soon we'll be in Oxford.

3   You see?

'Na, gut. Es is mir ganz égale. Aber, wenn Wir weiter so fahren, sicher werden Wir Mittagessen in Birmingham.'[1]

After these belligerent exchanges, the confrontation went into a different gear. Suddenly uncle roared:

'Enriquez, stop the automobile, now!'

Out of the corner of my eye I could now see the driver's ashen face – possibly wondering, with no references, where he could get a new job. Finally, having found a suitable gap on the motorway, Enriquez steered the ambassadorial Mercedes onto the hard shoulder. Now, Uncle addressed his son directly:

'Get out of the car, insolent young man, and start walking back to the embassy!' My cousin, equally defiant, replied:

'With pleasure.'

As the motorway traffic whizzed passed us, and the ambassadorial car stood still at the hard shoulder, uncle roared again:

'Rauss! Marche-marche!'[2] As my cousin was about to step out of the car. I whispered, 'Don't be silly.'

It was no use. He was already out of the car, standing on the hard shoulder. Now, observing the stalemate, my uncle's wife intervened. Laced with a heavy Turkish accent, she pleaded in French:

'Ce n'est qu'un enfant.'[3] Uncle retorted,

'Et sans aucun respect!'[4]

---

1 Suit yourself. But if we travel any further, we'll be having lunch in Birmingham.

2 Out! March!

3 He's only a kid.

4 And with no respect whatsoever!

At the end, what saved the day was, benefiting from this unscheduled stop, Enriquez had a chance to consult a map. Also, realising this impasse required a scapegoat in order to give a chance to the belligerent parties to 'retrieve with Honour', he confessed:

'Excellenz, I make mistake.'

Happy to find a scapegoat, uncle told Enriquez 'not to worry', and came out of the showdown looking the 'magnanimous employer'.

My cousin, equally relieved about not having to walk back to London, quietly slipped back into the Mercedes – although not without a smile, reflecting his Phrygian victory.

Enriquez, in no time, found a roundabout and got the car travelling in the right direction.

In fact, in order to regain all the uselessly clocked up miles, he put his foot down. Consequently, we were now travelling at a neat 70 mph – this time, towards London.

Mercifully with the crisis blown over, the mood in the car had changed again. Uncle even started flirting, once more, with the sexy violinist.

'I hope this mishap didn't upset you... Enriquez is from Portugal.'

So, after half an hour's back paddling, we were finally driving through the gates of The Hurlingham. However, what I did not know was that the day had a few more surprises in store for us or, to be precise, for my uncle.

* * *

The interior of The Hurlingham was what, with hindsight, I would describe as an English stately home. The restaurant, overlooking the gardens, was a large, ornate, Edwardian room – with high ceilings adorned with Ormolu figurines.

Being Sunday, it was a full house with members of the high 'Establishment' of English society.

Noticing my wonderment, as if speaking to me but, in reality, for the benefit of the sexy violist, uncle explained:

'This is a most exclusive club in London'; casually adding, 'Ambassadors are members automatically…'

'Welcome, Your Excellency', said the Maître D. handing us the menus.

Now, uncle was in his element – advising our sexy violinist what to order:

'My Dearest, on Sundays, roast-beef and Yorkshire pudding is the traditional English dish to have.'

Even my cousin seemed to have put the unfortunate incident on the motorway behind himself and, by now, was eagerly eyeing the carving trolley.

So, once more, life was beautiful, or so it seemed – until the Maître D. was ready to take our orders.

Although uncle had not yet cracked the English language one hundred percent, he suddenly embarked on patriotic flag-waiving – extolling the virtues of our sexy violinist. Only, he thought if he slightly perverted German he spoke English:

'For mein Sohn, he will have ein soup, roast beef, und Coca Cola.'

Then came the commercial:

'Und, für unserer sehr berhümte geigenspielerin die, als Ich in Moscow Botschafter war, mit David Oistrakh studierte, und morgen abend, in der Festival Hall, with Yehudi Menuhin die Bach Doppel Cocerto spielen wird.'[1]

---

1   Vaguely translated: 'And… for our distinguished violinist who studied with David Oistrakh, when I was ambassador in Moscow; and who will be performing the Bach Double Concerto, with Yehudi Menuhin at the Festival Hall, tomorrow evening.'

Now, I could see, the Maître D. desperately striving to figure out what was demanded of him. But it was no use. So, he most diplomatically stated:

'I'm sorry Your Excellency, we don't seem to have that on the menu today.'

Suddenly, there was a hush at the table. My aunt, remaining calm, portrayed 'indifference with dignity'. As for myself, focused my eyes onto an imaginary fly on the wall.

A minute later the hush came to an abrupt end – with the entire restaurant of The Hurlingham Club reverberating to the coquettish, almost hysterical, laughter of our sexy violinist. It was a crisp chuckle, as if the beautiful chandelier above us had been shattered, and million pieces of crystal were raining onto the crème de la crème of the English society, enjoying their Sunday Roast. Then, with a sudden swerve of her head, shoving off her long blonde hair, she announced:

'What an anecdote! I must mention it this evening, in my interview on the BBC.'

After that, the day was lost for good. Uncle's humour never returned. Although he did try to look affable, the chill in the air never left us.

As for myself, for the first time in my life, I realised how cruel women could be. Mind you, don't you think, with their narrow shoulders, tiny waists, and slightly larger hips, they do look like a violin – some even a Stradivarius.

DARLING

To Freddie Raphael

Her blond hair ran almost down to her waist, and with her shapely legs, protruding from her Deutsche Schule uniform, she looked even more enticing.

She was sixteen and I was fourteen – Sixteen-year-old girls simply did not socialise with fourteen-year-old boys. At that part of one's life, even a one year age difference meant almost a generation gap. Of course, the fact that my parents still made me wear shorts, did not help matters either.

Anyway, forget about 'socialising', I would consider myself lucky, if I managed to get as much as a vague smile from her, when, occasionally, she and I shared the lift in the block of flats where we lived, in Nisantasi, the posh neighbourhood of 1960s Istanbul.

Her name was Zeynep. She was the dentist's daughter who lived in the flat below.

Occasionally, she kept her blond hair in a chignon. With her huge green eyes which shined behind her black rimmed spectacles, and her blond hair pulled back, not only did she look sophisticated, but outright sexy. In fact, in her Deutsche Schule blazer, with the school coat of arms – a heroic eagle against the German flag, she could almost have been German.

Sometimes, I used to run into her on her way back from school; or, to be precise, I would lie in wait at the corner of our block of flats, and pretend to run into her. Then, we would walk down the street, chatting about the movie playing at our local cinema.

'Did you see the new Billy Wilder?'

More often than not, she would give me a dejected look as if to say, 'At your age, what do you know about movies?'

On other occasions, we shared the lift. Standing next to her in such close proximity and smelling her young body, I would torment thinking if she, in turn, could hear my pounding heart. By the time we reached her flat on the fourth floor, I used to feel kind of sea-sick.

Of course, as far as she was concerned, I was no more than the neighbours' boy, living in the flat above. I was sure, if someone had asked her if I was blond or had dark hair, fat or slim, she could not tell. Mercifully, soon after my fourteenth birthday, I was dispatched to England and, with that, my suffering came to an end.

It was not until some twelve years later, Zeynep reappeared in my life. By then, of course, a lot of water had passed under the bridge.

I, for example, having scrapped through university with a mediocre second in International Relations, had dropped the idea of joining the Turkish Ministry of Foreign Affairs, and now was trying my hand at film producing. Given I had no experience of the latter either, I was desperately looking for funding. It was on one of those occasions, a Turkish friend of mine, passing through London, mentioned a 'young Turkish woman in Zurich', married to a mega-rich Swiss banker.

'What's more', my friend added, 'the guy's father is the chairman of Credit Suisse. They're loaded!'

'Who is she?'

'Her name is Zeynep. You wouldn't know her, you've been away too long.' Trying to sound casual, I asked,

'How come *you* know her?'

'Her father was my dentist.'

There was no need for further questioning. As I was trying to regain my composure, my friend scribbled on a piece of paper a telephone number, underlining the word Zurich and handed it over to me.

'You never know, this might get you the money for your movie.'

* * *

It took me well over a week to garner the courage to make the call to Zurich. I kept wondering if she would remember me as 'the fourteen year old in his shorts', if she remembered me at all...

'Of course I remember you!', said the sultry voice on the telephone, 'I hear you've become a big-shot film producer.'

'A slight exaggeration', I replied.

However, after that, the ice was broken. Her voice sounded exactly the same when she was sixteen – pure and fresh. I was in cloud number nine. However, any minute she would ask me the purpose of my call. What could I say? 'I'm after your husband's money!'

She was married into one of the richest families in the world, surely also rubbing shoulders with that ilk, and I scraping the barrel. As I was thinking how to end the call before making a total fool of myself, she cut me in mid-sentence:

'I'll be in London next week, let's do lunch.'

Somehow, I managed to give her my phone number.

'I'll call the moment I get in', she said. With that, she was gone.

I spent the rest of the week in a state of panic. First port of call was Turnbull & Asser on Jermyn Street, where I got six shirts and a bundle of new ties. Then I popped over to Simpsons on Piccadilly, those days, an upmarket men's wear store, and bought a new double-breasted blazer, with a couple of trousers. Now, I was no longer the fourteen-year-old in shorts!

Then I wondered, what was the purpose of this shopping spree – just for a lunch with a married woman whom I had not seen for over ten years? Besides, was it not her husband I was really after, so that I could fund my film?

However, while debating the morality of exploiting my first love in this way, when I returned home I found a message on my answering machine:

'Arriving tomorrow, come to The Dorchester at 7 pm. Ciao darling.'

Obviously, the lunch had become dinner. So I called San Lorenzo's, those days a trendy restaurant in London, and booked a table for two at 7:30 pm. However, one word kept reverberating in my head: 'Darling'.

'You must meet Caspar, he'll get you the finance for your film. He knows everybody.'

This was her openers, as we started sipping our Dry Martinis at San Lorenzo's. Then she added,

'He's flying in tomorrow.'

'Surely, he must have other things on his mind', I replied, trying to play it cool.

'Not in the slightest, he's just coming to spend the weekend with me. Then he's off to New York.'

The rest of the dinner was spent with some catching up. Zeynep looked as fresh as the day I left her behind, in Istanbul, twelve years ago – only, now more sensuous and sophisticated. She was very good at putting me at ease. In no time she got me yapping about why, after uni, I had decided not to return to Turkey – to join the Turkish Ministry of Foreign Affairs, causing a considerable rift between my father and myself.

She had a few skeletons in the cupboard herself. When I asked her how she met Caspar, she told me it was literally by accident on the

14

ski slopes of St. Moritz: While she was descending, she skid and hurt her ankle, and Caspar, like a knight in shining armour, appeared out of nowhere to help out.

'It was meant to happen,' she sighed then adding, indignantly: 'Where was my husband? At the Chalet, nursing a cold.'

'Your husband?'

'It wasn't a real marriage, darling, lasted only three months.'

She lit a cigarette and smiled, as if the whole thing was an insignificant detail.

By the time we got out of San Lorenzo's it was past ten o'clock. On Beauchamp place, I hailed a cab and told the driver to head for The Dorchester.

As the we drove along Knightsbridge, I was sill musing about her dumping her first husband three months into their marriage in order to nail the Swiss banker. As the cab turned into Park Lane, she said,

'We have so much to catch up, Darling. Let's go some place where we can listen to music, have a drink and chat some more…'

The Saddle Room, a fashionable club in 1970s London, was a unique establishment. It had the atmosphere of an English country house, blended with French sophistication. This was probably due to the fact that its owner, a certain Hélène Cordet, one time actress, was reputed to have been the mistress of the Duke of Edinburgh. Hence, I imagine, the English Country House theme – photographs of Derby winners, Jockeys, horses, Grand National cups… adorning the venue. However, the music was decidedly French: Charles Aznavour, Édith Piaf, Gilbert Bécaud… Consequently, The Saddle Room's clientele were mostly rich Middle Eastern playboys.

'Darling, I absolutely love it', Zeynep said, as we settled down at our table, in the shape of a barrel, by the dance floor.

The smell of whisky and cigarettes must have relaxed her even more as, I noticed, while we were chatting, her hand reached for mine, and she started teasing it with her finger-tips. Now, in this darkly lit disco, against the strains of Aznavour, looking at Zeynep, I could almost see the sixteen year old girl, with her long blond hair down to her waist, in her Deutsche Schule uniform. Only, now she was all the more sensuous and desirable. As another Aznavour song filled the disco.

'Shall we dance?' She sighed.

On the dance floor, I got the strange feeling she was more than friendly. First I thought it was my imagination but, no mistake, she was definitely coming on to me. Then, wrapping her arms around me, she whispered into my ear,

'You used to fancy me, didn't you, back in those days...'

As if to apologise, I mumbled,

'I was only fourteen.'

'I always knew you'd grow up to be a handsome man.'

It was obvious where she was going with this, and I saw little point in resisting.

'You were already the most sexy woman on earth', I replied, as our lips met to the strains of Charles Aznavour's 'Hier Encore, j'avais vingt ans...'

* * *

The next morning, when I woke up to the canter of horses passing by, outside my flat in Lowndes Square, I had to pinch myself to make sure I was not dreaming. However, there she was, Zeynep, sleeping by my side, with her golden blond hair spread onto the pillow. We had hardly slept during the night, as if to make-up for the lost years.

'Oh my God, Horses!', she sighed, opening her eyes, then adding,

'I could easily live in London...'

With that, she put her arms around me, and our lips met once more. We made love all day, then nodding off, then starting all over again.

16

Finally, I woke up with the phone ringing. Given it was early January, it had already gotten dark early.

'It's Caspar. Sorry to disturb you, do you know where my wife is?', asked the voice, with a German accent, at the other end.

Feeling as if he could see us, I immediately pulled the cover over us. However, totally impervious to the circumstances, putting her arms around me, Zeynep placed her head on my shoulder. The proximity of her head to the receiver was more than alarming. In order to let her know who was calling, I spoke loudly,

'Oh hello, Caspar...' He continued,

'I just flew in. I'm at the Dorchester. Zeynep told me, she was going have to dinner with you. I thought you... might know.'

I was about to lie: 'Haven't got the foggiest', but Zeynep beat me to it. She spoke right into the receiver:

'Hallo, Darling. Ich bin in Knightsbridge, Ich komme ja Schon. Tschüss.'

She then placed her head back on my shoulder. By now, absolutely certain that Caspar had got the picture, I quickly put the phone down.

'You're mad!', I exclaimed, in a huff.

'Just relax', she replied, putting her arms around me.

In order to calm myself, I said to myself, this was probably how the 'Jet Set' lived: they were not bound by middle class morality.

Still, a terrifying thought occurred to me. What if Caspar jumped in a cab and came right over! I could almost imagine a scene, like in a Turkish movie, the cuckolded husband pulling a gun and shooting the unfaithful wife or, into the bargain, also the lover!

'I don't wish to appear inhospitable, but hadn't you better get dressed?' I mumbled, trying to sound calm.

'Aren't you coming?'

'Coming where?'

17

'Why, to The Dorchester, of course!'

'Are you crazy?'

'Don't be so bourgeois.'

As she disappeared into the bathroom, I took stock of the situation. Obviously, I could kiss goodbye to any funding for my film. Only an idiot would have failed to cotton on to what was going on; and Caspar, a shrewd Swiss banker, surely, was not one. As she came out of the bathroom, Zeynep asked,

'Why aren't you dressed?'

'I'm not coming, period!'

* * *

As we arrived at The Dorchester, Caspar greeted me with a hearty handshake.

'I heard so much about you!'

He spoke with a heavy German accent which, I felt, he did not make the slightest effort to correct. He looked a typical Swiss banker, a nondescript face with thick black rimmed glasses. He was professionally polite.

Zeynep, now coquettish, was showering her husband with little kisses.

Over dinner, at The Dorchester restaurant, Caspar ordered a 1952 Gevrey Chambertin. Although I was on tender hooks, Zeynep did not have a hair out of place. Now holding my hand, she said:

'Darling, tell Caspar about your movie.'

'I wouldn't want to bore him…'

'Don't be silly!'

So, the rest of the evening was spent with me pitching my film to Caspar. Only, in the last twenty-four hours having bedded his wife, I got the story-line all muddled up, and missed the punchlines. Still, Caspar was courteous,

'Fascinating! When do you plan to shoot?'

How could I say, 'It all depends on you'.

'They haven't got the money yet', Zeynep came to my rescue, adding, 'Surely, you can help?'

I was saved by the waiter wanting to take our orders for desserts.

'I'm dieting', I mumbled, wanting to get out of there as quickly as possible.

As I was bidding them goodnight, on the steps of The Dorchester, Caspar said he was flying to New York in the morning, as he had a meeting on Wall Street the same day.

'In fact, with someone who might be interested in your film', he added.

'I'm going to the airport with Caspar, only, I'll fly back to Zurich. So, I'll say goodbye too', said Zeynep, giving me a quick kiss on the lips.

As the cab drove on, I could see them, on the steps of The Dorchester, waving goodbye.

The next day, Sunday, I took stock of the situation, and wondered how things might unfold. Were we, Zeynep and I, going to embark on an affair, behind her husband's back? How would this pan out, with her living in Zurich, and I in London? Or… was this a 'one night stand' of sorts. As I was debating all the permutations, the phone rang.

'I need to see you, come to The Dorchester at once!'

Why was she still in London? From the tone of her voice I could feel something was seriously wrong. Could she have spilled the beans, as in admitting to having spent the night and most of the following day, with me? Thinking of my own safety, I asked:

'Is Caspar gone?'

'Good riddance, Darling!'

When I arrived at The Dorchester, I quickly made for her suite. As I rung the door bell, I was bracing myself for the worst. Obviously,

Caspar had cottoned on to what was going on, and she confessed. The question was how had he reacted to it? The fact that I blew my chances of funding my film was the least of my problems. However, I was in for a surprise.

As soon as I stepped in, Zeynep grabbed a bundle of papers from the dressing table and shoved them in my face—

'Look!'

I picked them up from the thickly carpeted floor. They looked like letters, written in German, all on expensive stationary, drafted in an ornate, elaborate handwriting. They were addressed to Caspar, and all started with 'Mein Schatz', 'Liebling' or with such terms of endearment. I looked at the name of the signatory – it was one 'dein' Veronica. Obviously, these were love letters from a woman called Veronica, to Caspar. Still, feigning ignorance, I declared,

'They're in German…'

'Cut the bullshit, you understand German perfectly!' Zeynep hissed,

'He's having an affair with that *bitch*!'

'Who?'

'Veronica, of course, who do you think!' Then, lighting a cigarette, she added: 'My best friend…'

How had these highly toxic letters come to be in Zeynep's possession I did not know, nor did I really wanted to know.

'Probably a flash in a pan', I said, trying to comfort her.

'It's been going on over a year! They are making plans! Here, see for yourself!'

She once more threw the letters in my direction.

'He bought her a duplex in Trump Tower!' Her moods oscillated from shock to malice.

'She certainly knows how to sell herself!'

After I calmed her down, I managed to get some background information.

'The bitch told me she was opening an art gallery in New York. She used to work at Sotheby's in Zurich, so I suspected nothing.'

Then, once more, she turned on Caspar:

'I did always wonder why you do all the travelling to New York!'

I realised, this had put the lid on my film being funded by Caspar, for good.

'Meeting at Goldman Sachs, ideal guy for your film... Such fucking crap!'

'Actually, I'm relieved.'

'What do you mean?'

'Well, under the circumstances...'

'What circumstances?'

Obviously, it had never occurred to her that, only twenty-four hours previously, she had committed the same misdemeanour with me as she now was accusing her husband of. Still, I knew, this was hardly the moment for moral comparisons. So, I replied,

'I don't know what I'm talking about.'

'I will make him pay for this!' She hissed, pouring herself a large whisky.

Without thinking, I spoke again:

'How?'

'I don't know yet, but sure as hell, I'll find a way!'

* * *

An entire week passed and I had not heard from Zeynep – now, mercifully, back in Zurich. Given the drama, to which I had become an unwitting participant, had taken larger proportions, I was not entirely unhappy to have a period of reprieve. I even hoped, with time, things might sort themselves out – as, in life, they had a habit of doing. Still, the picture of Zeynep in my bed, with her harvest gold mane spread onto my pillow, kept cropping up in my mind. Inevitably I wondered, now that her husband was having a full blown affair himself, what was there to stop us?

I was woken up from my daydreaming by the phone ringing. It was Zeynep. I was about to say I'd been missing her, but she cut to the chase:

'I'm divorcing the son of a bitch!'

Then came the nitty gritty: The villa, (on the shores of Lake Zurich), she explained, was in her name anyway, as Caspar had given it to her as their wedding present. However, she then went for a more jocular approach:

'You studied law, let me read you something.'

I do not think she even heard me when I pointed out what I studied was International Law – governing relationships between countries, and not between husbands and wives, seeking divorce.

Regardless, she proceed to read – in German. As she went along, I realised it was a 'Deed of Gift'. She kept repeating a certain clause numerous times, and finally asked,

'What do you think?'

With my limited German, all I could gather was this 'Act of Gift' included 'fixtures and fittings'. In English, this would mean light switches, the dishwasher, the oven and the such like. However, Zeynep's take on this was slightly different.

In her opinion, 'fixtures and fittings' meant the canvasses on the walls – original Manet's, Monet's, a Degas, a few Picasso's and Chagall's. In effect, their aggregate value was probably well over the real estate value of the six bed room villa, sitting on the shores of Küsnacht, the part of Zurich often referred to as 'Gold Küste', (Gold Coast), due to the number of billionaires residing there.

This time, I did not play 'I don't speak German' card, as I knew she would not fall for it. Instead, to have a quick get away, I said this was not something one could resolve over the phone – soon realising I walked into another hole. Without hesitation, she replied:

'Take the next flight and come over.'

Caspar was in New York – now indefinitely, so I could stay at the villa. I replied, I could not fly out to Zurich 'just like that'. Zeynep sighed,

'I need some affection.'

When I arrived at the villa, in Zurich, the following day, I was treated to a conducted tour of the canvasses adorning the walls – two Mone'ts, a Manet, a Lautrec, a couple of Degas', and a number of Chagall's and Picasso's.

'Caspar's father got them for a song, during the war', Zeynep explained.

It was, by any standards, an amazing collection. There was, however, one item, a Degas which hit the spot with me – 'Après le bain, femme s'essuyant la nuque'. It was not even an oil painting, but a pastel sketch on paper. Still, for me, it eclipsed all the other priceless oils on the walls. I had seen it, in various versions, in art books, as Degas had done a number of sketches as dry run for an oil painting, but I had never seen the original, not even in any museum. Now, I was looking at it, and it simply was breath taking – the light, the feeling of movement, and the subdued eroticism…

At that point I thought, the trip to Zurich had not been a waste, if only to see this Degas drawing.

'They're all are mine!' Flagging the Deed of Gift, Zeynep announced: 'Fixtures and fittings included.'

I realised, at this stage, some diplomacy was required.

'Maybe you ought to seek professional advise.'

'What do you mean?'

'Talk to a lawyer.'

'They'll side with him!'

'Why?'

'You know the Swiss – when it comes to money…'

'You might be right', I replied. She did have a point.

'So, *are* you going to help or not?', she asked, now impatient.

'But how?'

'Go to Avis and rent a van.'

What are you talking about?' I asked, mystified.

'We take down the paintings, and you drive them to Liechtenstein.'

'Why Liechtenstein?'

'It is outside Swiss jurisdiction.'

For a moment I wondered if this was all an elaborate joke. However, the look in Zeynep's beautiful cobalt-blue eyes told me she meant business – in every inch of the way.

There it was, this divinely gorgeous woman, sitting in front of me in her Givenchy dress, wearing a four string pearl necklace, talking to me, all calm, like a professional criminal planning the next bank job. She crossed her legs, casually letting her tight skirt exhibit more of them and, and dangling her Balmain shoes, she sighed,

'I need a man by my side…'

Avoiding her gaze, I pretended to study the canvasses on the wall.

'Après le bain, femme s'essuyant la nuque… Degas did that in 1898. It was a sketch for the oil painting', I mumbled.

'There's an Avis garage round the corner, go and get the van', she answered. 'If you hurry, you could be in Liechtenstein before five.'

It was this last remark which alerted me to the possibility that the whole operation might have been planned well in advance.

'Why before five?'

'Because, the banks close at five!'

Then, she took out a map from the drawer and laid it out on the dinner the table.

'There's no need for you to drive through Zurich. Just stay on this side of the lake, and follow your nose', she said, pointing her finger on the map.

'We're here. Head for Rapperswil. There, you will pick up the A3. Then aim for Bad Ragaz. Just before you get there, you will leave the Autobahn, for Vaduz. It's all sign posted.'

'Aren't you coming?' I asked, as if I had agreed to go along with this grand larceny.

'I have a hair appointment.'

'What will I do, when I get to Vaduz, with half the Musée d'Orsay in the van?'

'When you get there, you will be met.'

That sounded even more ominous. She wrote neatly on a piece of paper, a name and a phone number.

'Gunther is a friend from St. Moritz. He's gay, but adores me. He lives with his boyfriend, Helmut. He's the one who works at the Bank in Liechtenstein.'

'What bank?' I asked.

Zeynep giggled in her unique sultry way, casually throwing her long blond her behind.

'It's the name of the bank, you silly thing!'

'What do you mean?'

'Bank in Liechtenstein – that's the name of the bank.'

Obviously, Zeynep had not wasted a minute since she returned to Zurich from London. The heist – as that is what it was – had been planned with Swiss-like precision,

'What if I am stopped at the frontier?'

'There are no frontier checks between Switzerland and Liechtenstein.'

'How decent of them', I said, lost for words.

Still, what I just heard was the 'perfect crime', if there ever was one. Canvasses, worth millions of dollars, snatched in broad daylight, driven within hours to another country – a tax haven, with no frontier checks, and placed in a bank vault with a numbered account – with no name attached to it. All this, while the real culprit was having her hair done!

Of course, when Caspar returned from New York, having spent some quality time with his mistress, he might notice the walls of the villa, which once looked like Musée d'Orsay, were now somewhat blank. At that point, there could be two scenarios: Number one, the missing canvasses could become just another chess piece in game of an acrimonious divorce proceedings; number two: Caspar would simply contact the police.

It was the latter, to my horror I realised, the charge of grand larceny, which Zeynep was covering herself against. This was her insurance policy. That is, if Caspar did go to the police, she had the perfect alibi: at the established time of the crime, she was at her Coiffeur, having her hair done!

After all, *who* rented the van from Avis? When was it taken out? When was it returned? What was the mileage on the clock – equivalent to a return trip from Zurich to Liechtenstein! When were the canvasses were last seen? Then she said,

'If I don't take them, he'll give them all to the bitch!'

'The bitch?', I asked stupidly.

'Veronica, of course!', she hissed. 'You don't think she's in this just for a penthouse in Trump Tower, do you?'

That was when I realised these were different people. They played 'big'. My eyes discreetly wondered in her direction. In a way, she looked as pure and fresh as when she was sixteen, in her Deutsche Schule uniform. I wondered, if her trip to London was a part of the scam.

She lit another cigarette, crossing her legs at a different angle, exposing more of them, and browsing through a copy of the Vogue magazine, waiting for me to take the bait.

I wanted to laugh. Yes, I wanted to laugh at this picture of a most beautiful creature, now portraying the 'wronged wife'. I wanted to laugh, laugh out loud but, what do you know, I could not. Instead, I felt the warm tears running down my cheeks. In fact, I was still the fourteen year old boy, wearing shorts… Embarrassed, I quickly ran out of the room, on my way, managing to hit a small table and knock over an expensive Limoges vase which crashed into pieces on the shiny parquet floor.

In the street, I was cursing her Deutsche Schule uniform, our encounters in the lift, the flirtations on the way home – discussing the latest Billy Wilder movie… The whole damned thing.

* * *

When I returned to London, I erased all references to her from my address book, hoping, in the process, to erase her also out of my heart. I am not sure if I was entirely successful in the latter enterprise; but, for some years, I did manage not to think of her – at least consciously.

Until, one day, in Harrods, I saw a slender woman in the distance with long harvest gold hair, down to her waist, in an elegant dress. Sure enough it was her. I tried to quickly lose myself in the crowd, but she too must have seen me, for she quickly caught up:

'Darling!' she shouted.

As she put her arms around me, and giving me a kiss on the lips, she said,

27

'Where have you been hiding?'

After some polite chit-chat, I could not help asking if she and Caspar were now divorced.

'What on earth for?', she asked, surprised at my question.

'I thought, the Trump Tower, and…' She laughed:

'Water under the bridge.'

'And Veronica?'

'I decided to forgive them both.'

'That's mighty generous', I said, a tad sarcastic.

'Actually, Caspar was the generous one.'

'He was?'

'Yes, he gave me all the paintings – as a gift for taking him back.'

'He did?'

'This time all on the level, my lawyer sorted it out.'

'Including 'Après le Bain' by Degas?'

'That's only a sketch, darling.'

'Painted in 1898. It was done by Degas's girlfriend, Mademoiselle Charlotte Allegret', I added.

With that, we said our goodbyes, and I let her get on with her shopping in Harrods.

I still remember the puzzled look on her face, as to why I should attach such importance to a mere sketch.

THE MINK COAT

It was reddish brown, with a sheen, and it ran all the way down to Mrs Stone's ankles. Agnes Stone was my girlfriend Margot's mother. Given she was a portly lady, I cannot imagine how many minks it must have taken to produce the garment. However, in spite of being 'fifty something', and no oil painting, once enwrapped in this impressive coat, Mrs Stone looked 'a million dollars'.

Margot, her daughter, was a world class soprano, under contract to the Vienna State Opera. I had met her at the Royal Opera House, Covent Garden in 1970s, while I was an assistant stage director. Margot, on the other hand, was singing the title role in Verdi's La Traviata, one of the most difficult soprano parts in operatic repertoire.

Although only in her late twenties, she had already sung at the most prestigious houses in the world – Vienna, La Scala, Berlin Staatsoper, the Met, and now she was at Covent Garden. Margot had studied at Musik Hochschule in Vienna, and, due to an enormously voluminous voice, her career had enjoyed a meteoric rise.

Margot was South African, with a Jewish-Lithuanian father and Scottish mother – the proud owner of the mink coat. In fact the real family name was not 'Stone' but Stein, or Steinberg to be precise – due to her Jewish-Lithuanian father. On the other hand, Mrs Stone was quite proud of her Scottish ancestry – maintaining, she was related to the Queen. In her thick Scottish accent, laced with Afrikaans, she would explain,

'Her Majesty and I had tea together, when we in Cape Town.'

Margot, embarrassed, would whisper,

'And three hundred other guests at the embassy Garden Party.'

As for 'Margot', that was not her real name either. Her mother had decided, for one destined for operatic greatness, 'Deidre' was hardly a name to conjure up the desired effect – so Margot was born.

The Stones, on the whole, were harmless people. They were the product of the 1960s Zeitgeist in South Africa. They could hardly be blamed if they held slightly different views about this world, from the rest of us.

Margot had grown up in a farm near Durban, 'with thousands of acres of land', and hundreds of 'natives' living on it. Naturally, I did wonder why the Stones needed so many servants; or, more to the point, how could they afford them?

'The natives are happy to have a roof over their head', Margot would explain, proudly.

'Natives?', I enquired. Margot would laugh and translate,

'Blacks.'

'And do they work for free?'

'Are we supposed to pay them as well feed them?' She questioned.

But wait, I was going to tell you about the mink coat. As I said, Mrs Stone was so proud of it that, even in the middle of August, she would not be seen without it, saying,

'After South Africa, England feels so chilly.'

Now, you might wonder why a world famous opera singer would spend time with an assistant stage director – namely myself. The answer was simple. With compliments of his generous father, the assistant owned an apartment in London's fashionable Belgravia.

Moreover, by staying there, Margot would receive, the equivalent of what the Royal Opera would have paid out to the Savoy, for a suite, while she was performing in London. There was, however, a slight problem. Barring a half broken sofa and an armchair, the assistant's flat had no furniture, except a Steinway grand.

While I found this Spartan existence rather bohemian, Mrs Stone, Margot's mother, was hardly amused about having her celebrity daughter living almost in 'student digs'. Consequently, she constantly campaigned to get me to refurbish the flat, to 'make it fit for a Diva'. Things finally came to a head with an unexpected event.

One afternoon, Margot and her mother turned up, both in a huff.

'You have no idea what happened!'

This was Mrs Stone's standard opening, when she wanted to have the undivided attention of her audience. Invariably, that 'extraordinary event' would turn out to be, someone recognising her daughter in Harrods or Harvey Nichols, and asking her for an autograph. As usual, feigning 'suspense with anticipation', I asked.

'Oh, do tell…'

This time, however, I was in for a real surprise. Mrs Stone, took out a brown envelope from the pocket of her mink coat and placed it on the table.

'Here!'

'What is it?'

'Open it!'

When I did, I realised, the envelope was stashed with crisp £20 notes – at a glance , at least, £1,000.

'That's a fortune' I said, puzzled.

'£2,000' Mrs Stone replied.

Given in 1974, this was a small fortune, I was trying to figure out what all this was about.

'We found it in the taxi.'

This was the upshot: In common with all opera singers, Margot regularly visited a throat specialist. So, on that fateful morning, mother and daughter were on their way to see an ENT consultant in Harley Street. However, as they settled down in a cab, Mrs Stone felt a thick object by the side of her mink coat. Lifting the coat, underneath it, she found a brown envelope, and when she opened it, out poured £2,000 Sterling – in crisp £20 notes.

'So, there…' Mrs Stone concluded her story.

'Shouldn't you hand it over to the Carriage Office?'

'Don't be silly', she replied, 'They'd pocket it themselves', adding, 'I didn't steal it, I merely found it.' Then, with a smile, she announced, 'Besides, I am not going to keep it.'

'You'll give it to charity?'

'Not quite.'

'Oh?'

'*You* are going to have it.'

Knowing her, I knew there would be a catch:

'Why, Mrs Stone?'

'Because, my dear, I want you to furnish this flat.'

Suddenly, everything became clear. The whole story was made up – the cab, the mysterious brown envelope, the crisp £20 notes… This was her way of giving me £2,000 without hurting my Turkish pride, in order to get me buy furniture, so that her daughter could live in an apartment commensurate with her star status, where she could entertain without being embarrassed. Mrs Stone added,

'You are no longer a teenager, my dear.' Going along with the game, I replied,

'I still think you ought to return the money. Whoever lost it, is bound to go looking for it at the Carriage office.'

Mrs Stone would hear none of it. Irritated by my resistance, she replied,

'Who would carry £2,000 cash, in a brown envelope? Obviously, a drug dealer!'

'Maybe he was a hit-man, and this was the hush money...' Mrs Stone failed to see the sarcasm.

'More than likely!'

However, realising I had no intention of accepting the money, Mrs Stone took the envelope and placed it back into the pocket of her mink coat, hissing:

'As you wish, my dear.'

With that she sprung to her feet and made for the door. After she slammed the door behind her, I said to Margot.

'Nice try.'

'What're you talking about?'

'This cock and bull story?'

Margot screamed,

'What would it take to penetrate into your thick Turkish head that she did find the money in the cab and, out of the goodness of her heart, she was offering it to you!'

For the first time it occurred to me, she might, after all, be telling the truth.

'In that case, you must hand the money over to the Carriage Office', I said, adding, 'to keep it, will bring bad luck.'

On that note, no longer in speaking terms, we went to bed and pretended to fall asleep.

* * *

Almost a month passed and, by then, Margot was well into rehearsing La Traviata, Verdi's tragic opera about a hooker who falls in love with a middle-class hypocrite in 1850s Paris. It was a new production, starring also Luciano Pavarotti who, in 1970s, was the hottest tenor in the world. Consequently, all that eclipsed the case of the mysterious envelope in the cab.

Finally, the day of the premiere arrived and, since her husband was in Cape Town, it fell upon me to accompany Mrs Stone to the opera.

Needless to say, a premiere at the Royal Opera House was just the occasion to give the mink coat another airing. The fact that it was July and London was having a heatwave, had little bearing on the matter. Visibly sweating under the said garment, Mrs Stone looked even more ridiculous than usual. Be it as it may, she was the proud mother of a famous soprano, and she had to look the part.

However, when we arrived at Covent Garden, she did something quite out of character. Obviously, not relishing the prospect of sweating like mad during four acts of 'Traviata', she checked the mink coat into the cloak room. Then, she grumbled all the way to the auditorium,

'They should've given us a box!'

Mercifully, soon the lights were dimmed and, with the conductor in the pit, Mrs Stone's grumbling was cut short by Verdi's prelude to the tragic story of Marguerite Gautier. The first act went without a hitch. Indeed, with 'Folie, O Delirio Vano é Questo' Margot brought the house down and had to do an encore.

During the interval, I took Mrs Stone to the Crush Bar and gave her a glass of champagne. Soon, the General Administrator of Covent Garden spotted us and came over to congratulate Mrs Stone on her daughter's triumph. Then she was introduced to the chairman of the Board of Governors of the Royal Opera. Suddenly surrounded by the English Establishment, Mrs Stone was punch drunk with elation. Still, she whispered into my ear,

'I feel totally naked.'

* * *

Marguerite Gautier, as she was called in the original novel by Alexandre Dumas, the tuberculosis ridden heroine of Traviata, finally expired in the fourth act, and the curtain came down to a tumultuous applause, without a single dry eye left in the house. Margot alone took no less than nine curtain calls to screams of 'Bravi' as flowers rained down on her, thrown by her fans in the audience.

As we were leaving the auditorium, people from the South African High Commission caught up with Mrs Stone and congratulated her on her daughter's triumph. Mrs Stone held court until the auditorium was virtually empty, receiving compliments and felicitations.

Given this was a new production, there was an 'after party' at one of the five star restaurants in Covent Garden. As we were finally heading for the cloak-room to pick up her mink coat, Mrs Stone said,

'I'd better keep it on during dinner, it is getting chilly.'

It was at that point things started going pear shaped. When Mrs Stone handed the ticket to the cloak room attendant, a young coloured girl, she looked around and asked,

'What was the item?

'A mink coat', replied Mrs Stone, casually. The girl disappeared and came back.

'Are you sure you left it here?'

'Of course I'm sure!'

'There's nothing here.'

'Maybe it disappeared into thin air?', replied Mrs Stone, raising her voice.

As she became more irritated, her upper class English accent gave way to Afrikaans. The cloak room attendant pointed to a notice on the wall, reading it aloud:

'I don't care what it says!', yelled Mrs Stone, 'I want my mink!'

By now, the raised voices attracted the attention of Front of the House Manager, an effete man with a posh accent.

'Could I help, Madam?'

I quickly explained the situation. The Manager turned to the coloured cloak room attendant for clarification.

'Have a look', said the girl, 'there's nothing.'

'What do you expect', commented Mrs Stone, 'if you employ Rif-Raf like that at the Royal Opera House. Back home, they wouldn't be allowed to ride in the same bus as us!'

I whispered to Mrs Stone to keep her voice down.

'Why should I! That's why England isn't England anymore', she yelled at the effete man.

'You let them in, and they steal your mink coat!'

'I'm merely the Front of House Manager, Madam, I don't run the country', he replied, now pointing to the notice at the cloak room-

'The public are reminded...'

'I am *not* the public!', Mrs Stone roared,

'My daughter is the star of this opera. Without her, there would be no Royal Opera!'

As if to add insult to the injury, the manager replied,

'Madam, we have to go home too.'

In order to get Mrs Stone to leave the theatre, I pointed out, by now Margot must be at the 'After Party', and wondering what had happened to us. Finally we left, but not without Mrs Stone firing the last salvo.

'This is not the end of it, you know!'

As soon as we were in the street, she added,

36

'I'm frozen!'

Now, she was in no mood to attend the after party.

'How can I go looking like this?'

I offered to take her back home, but she insisted I went on my own.

'You cannot leave Margot alone.'

She did have a point there. For, if neither of us showed up, Margot could easily assume something had happened to her mother. As I put her in a cab, she delivered her last line:

'Enjoy yourselves, don't worry about me…'

When I finally made it to the restaurant, the party was in full swing. Seeing her mother was not with me, Margot feared the worst.

'Where's my mother?' She gasped.

Calming her down, I told her the story. I thought, realising there was nothing wrong with her mother health wise, she would be relieved. Margot shrieked,

'This is outrageous!'

I pointing out there was a notice at the cloakroom saying items left there were at the owners' risk, I added,

'Rules are rules.'

'Rules are for the public!'

'She is the public.'

'She is my mother and I am Margot Stone!'

'The thief does not know that.'

'Is that best you can say? What kind of man are you?'

Margot always felt, probably a South African thing, challenging a man's masculinity was the best way to get him do whatever she wished. Still, given by then most guests were seated, I suggested we joined them, as there was nothing else we could do.

'That's where you are wrong!', she hissed, as we took our seats.

On our way back home, in the limousine provided by the Royal Opera, we sat in silence. Similarly, when we got home, Margot went straight to bed without even saying goodnight.

As for myself, also in bed but wide awake, I kept philosophising. There was, after all, Divine Justice. Suddenly, the events of the past few weeks flashed through my mind. The mysterious £2,000, the refusal of Mrs Stone to hand the money over to the Lost Property Office. And now, the mink coat taking a walk. Maybe there was a God after all, who observed everything – rewarding the righteous and punishing the wrongdoers.

I wondered what was the price of the mink coat. Was it more, or less, than £2,000, the amount stashed into the brown envelope? As I was trying to quantify Divine Justice in terms of hard currency, I must have fallen asleep.

* * *

When I woke up it was already 9 am. I could hear Margot's voice, trained to fill a major opera house, coming from the sitting room. She was on the phone, I realised, talking to her mother:

'He is a wimp, what can I do?'

Under the circumstances, I thought it prudent not to wake up yet. So, as Margot walked into the bedroom, I closed my eyes again. I could hear her hissing—

'Typical!'

Mercifully, she quickly got dressed and, slamming the door, went out. Obviously, the 'War Cabinet' was being convened at her Mum's. There would be calls to South Africa, to consult with Mr Stone, worse still, with the brothers. Although I had never met them, I knew you did not mess with them. Their life philosophy was, Margot has explained, 'shoot first ask questions later'.

In the afternoon, Margot returned with her mother. By the angry look on their face, I could see 'the war cabinet' had achieved little. As soon as they arrived, they were back on the phone, this time, to South Africa. Overhearing them, I realised why they were in this foul mood.

Mother and daughter had gone to see Sir David Burlington, the General Manager of the Royal Opera, demanding full compensation for the disappearing mink coat. The bad news was, Sir David told them, if they were compensated Mrs Stone, this would create a precedent and thereafter, every person who claimed to have lost a garment would want compensation. Sir David had concluded,

'Besides, do we really know who took the mink coat?'

'She was tarred with a brush!'

Obviously, Sir David had pretended not to hear that remark, but Mrs Stone was not the type to mince her words.

'If we were in South Africa, by now she'd be languishing in prison. What's more, I would have my mink coat back!'

Finally ending the call to Sir David, exhausted, Mrs Stone collapsed on my half broken sofa – I was even worried she might have a heart attack! After all, she was hardly at bloom of youth. Although she claimed to be 50, I reckoned she was 60 if a day, and seriously overweight. I even felt guilty about my thoughts of the previous night – Divine Justice and the rest. Surely, she did not deserve to die for mis-appropriating the £2,000, instead of handing it over to the Carriage Office.

However, having got her breath back, soon Mrs Stone was her old self. Pointing her finger at me, she announced,

'*He* wished it on me!' Margot joined in,

'The wimp might take it lying down, but I won't! This is not the end of it!'

I did not take any of this personally. I knew they were upset and had to let off steam. Mercifully, the day after, there was the second performance of Traviata, and that took priority.

However, that evening, Mrs Stone, who had never missed a performance of her daughter's, declared she was feeling 'poorly' and preferred to stay at home. Besides, she had 'nothing to wear...' Luckily, this meant, I could attend the second performance on my own.

When she was singing, Margot normally arrived at Covent Garden about three hours before the performance. This gave her time to do her scales and arpeggios, put on her make-up and, as she used to emphasise, 'get into character'. Whereas, being a member of the public, I had no such restrains. I could arrive half an hour before curtain up and have a drink. So, that evening too, I had a vodka tonic at the Crush Bar, and waited for the bell signalling the performance was about to begin.

However, 7:30 pm came and went and there was no bell. This was highly irregular, given the Royal Opera was most punctual and performances started always on the dot. By 7:45 pm and still no bell, people were beginning to give each other asking looks. Finally, a posh voice came on the tannoy, announcing,

'Due to unforeseen circumstances tonight's performance will start at 8 pm.'

Obviously they had a technical problem. I ordered another vodka tonic and chatted with the Irish barman. Eventually, the bells started ringing, inviting the audience to take their seats. Finally the curtain went up, punctually half an hour late, at 8 pm.

Margot was in great form, hitting every note spot on, singing with great élan. In fact, she was probably giving one of her best performances. Once again, with 'Follie, O Delirio Vano' she brought the house down. The applause was tumultuous demanding an encore, and Margot duly obliged.

When Verdi's heroine, Violetta Valéry finally expired with tuberculosis and the curtain came down, I lost the count curtain calls Margot took.

At the stage door there were double the number of autograph hunters, and Margot, carrying a huge bouquet of flowers, duly obliged them. In fact, in spite of the fact she thoroughly disliked autograph hunters, now, she was even indulging them even with small chit-chat.

It was not until we were finally in the limousine, travelling back home, I asked about the late start of the performance.

'Technical problems?'

'Not quite' she replied. I could hear mischief in her voice. She continued without further ado.

'They coughed up the money for Mum's Mink Coat.'

Suddenly, the whole thing became crystal clear. How could I have been so blind! The late start, the exceptional performance, the tumultuous applause. However, I wanted to hear it from her own mouth. Feigning naivety, I asked:

'What do you mean?'

'God! Sometimes you really are stupid!'

So, this was the upshot. When, they had the traditional 30 minute call – alerting performers to 30 minutes to curtain up, Margot announced she suddenly had developed a sore throat, and could not possibly go on.

Given, in opera, if singers develop throat problems, those signs become obvious long before the last 30 minutes to curtain up – usually in the morning. However, now, there was no possibility whatsoever of replacing Margot. This meant one thing only: cancelling the performance and refunding the 1,500 strong audience. Given it was a full house, and La Traviata being a top tier ticket price, the financial losses would be colossal.

Naturally, within minutes of Margot's becoming 'indisposed', Sir David Burlington the General Administrator, was notified. By then it was almost 7:30 pm and Margot held all the aces.

It took Sir David about ten minutes to make his way to back stage. Once in Margot's dressing room, he casually announced, the management had reconsidered the case of the missing mink coat, and decided to reimburse her mother the full amount. Then, he discreetly placed on Margot's dressing table a duly signed cheque for £3,000.

While putting on finishing touches to her make-up, Margot casually remarked to Sir David:

'Why, I'd forgotten all about that.'

Sir David then asked if Margot could not make a special effort and go on.

'Why, I'm already feeling better. Obviously, it was a spasm', Margot replied.

* * *

By the time we got home, I was cursing Divine Justice, Providence, Hand of God, and the rest of it. In the event, not only Margot's mother had gotten to keep £2,000 she found in the cab, but walked away with a dividend.

'The funny thing is…', Margot said, as she was spraying herself with perfume before getting into bed,

'Mummy bought that Mink Coat in Cape Town for £1,000. Now, she made £2,000 profit.'

The following season, Margot returned to Covent Garden in 'Macbeth', another Verdi piece. As Lady Macbeth she was sensational, breaking all house records with the number of curtain calls she took.

Sadly, by then, she and I were no longer an item. So, I had to content myself to admire her performance, from my seat in the balcony, as a member of the public.

Still, perhaps great artists are best admired from a distance; getting to know them up close and personal might be somewhat disappointing.

MY FATHER'S FRIENDS

My father was a paper and pulp broker in 1960s Istanbul. He supplied newsprint – the actual paper newspapers are printed on. Since newspapers appeared daily, newsprint to them was like oxygen to humans, which meant father became quite well off in no time. A by-product of this was, he could now afford to send his son – myself, to be educated in England.

So, that is how I ended up at the French Lycée in South Kensington; then, in early 1970s, at University College London, studying International Law – a disciple I had little belief in. On the other hand, living in London meant I was often exposed to father's friends, his clients, wanting all sorts of favours – shopping or being accompanied to the doctors.

In fact, going up and down Harley Street with visiting Turks, soon I got to know the ailments of everybody in Istanbul – who was suffering with an enlarged prostate, who had diabetes, who had cardiovascular problems, etc.

However, let's not digress, I was going to tell you about a certain Mr Rona, a man in his late fifties, the chief editor of an important Turkish daily – consequently, dad's best client. Moreover, being the chief editor, Mr Rona also had his own weekly column, penning articles about morality and family values. He also liked watching pornography.

All the same, among all my father's friends I liked Mr Rona best. Probably, this had something to do with the fact that he was a writer of sorts, whereas all of my father's friends were hard nosed businessmen, interested only in money.

Moreover, Mr Rona must have sensed that I had a soft spot for him, as his visits to London became more and more frequent.

Our daily routine started with me picking him up around 6 pm from his three star hotel on Wigmore Street – he was 'careful with money' and felt five-star hotels were pure self-indulgence. Then, we would head straight for Soho – home of pornographic movie theatres. Invariably, they were all located along narrow alleyways, with small nondescript doors, and neon lighting at the top, advertising 'Continental Movies', 'Scandinavian Films' or 'Art Cinema'. Then you saw another sign – 'Members Only'.

Needless to say, membership could be applied for and be approved, on the spot. It was a matter of filling a simple form, and doorman kindly obliged by seconding the application. In the process, I noticed, Mr Rona became 'Marcel Plume'.

I often wondered if 'Marcel Plume' was a 'porte-manteau', inspired by Marcel Proust, the French writer best known for his 'A La Recherche de Temps Perdu'. Mr Rado gave Monsieur Plume's address as Boulevard St Germain – the literary quarter of Paris, where other luminaries of French literature, Sartre, André Gide, Albert Camus, Simone de Beauvoir, Francoise Sagan also resided.

I used to feel slightly sorry for Mr Rona as, obviously, a Marcel Proust was what he would have liked to have been – a 'l'Homme de Lettres'. After all, Mr Rona himself had spent four years at the Sorbonne studying French literature. I could almost hear him saying to himself:

'All that toil at the Sorbonne, the thesis on Proust, and what do you have to show for it? Such is life, cruel and unrewarding…'

44

I think he felt, he should have been a 'Man of Letters' at least in Turkey, with a few novels under his belt, some translated into French, maybe receiving Prix Goncourt. Well, forget about receiving it, even a nomination would have done the trick. In fact, Mr Rado would have happily settled for a minor Turkish prize for literature.

However, the sad truth was, after a few attempts at penning a number of novels – rejected by every publisher, his literary talent was confined to writing his weekly column of cautionary tales, in his newspaper.

Be it as it may, while in some respects life may have been cruel to Mr Rona, in others, fortune had smiled at him. A Turkish Press Baron, who made his money in the black market during the war, had made him the editor of his major daily. Although this hardly won Mr Rado the Prix Goncourt, it afforded him a large apartment in the posh part of Istanbul, a Mercedes with a chauffeur, and a summer residence on one of the Princess Islands. This was further compounded when he married an unattractive but seriously wealthy woman.

In short, while his peers were 'still working on that novel' and did not know where their next meal was coming from, Mr Rado had become a respectable member of the Istanbul Bourgeoisie.

As I was musing about all this, we would be making our way into Art House movie theatres. The 'auditorium' of these cinemas were invariably damp basements, consisting of a few rows of casually put together chairs which never matched. Needles to say, the audience consisted purely of middle aged men, with their raincoats neatly folded on their laps, in order to camouflage the busy hands of their owners.

Since those days, in the early 1970s, smoking in cinemas was not yet disallowed, there was constant thick fog, highlighted by the narrow beam of the projector, giving the place an even a more sleazy atmosphere.

Mr Rona, watched these films by a crackling old projector, with great concentration, as if he was on a 'fact finding mission', occasionally commenting,

'Disgusting... Filthy... Repulsive...'

And that was the beginning of our evening.

After the movies, we would adjourn to a wine bar, where 'dinner' consisted of a bottle of cheap Australian Chardonnay and a piece of French camembert. Mr Rona could make a portion of Camembert last us an entire evening, during which he would recount stories and gossip about what was happening in Turkey – which politician was having an affair with which 'movie star'; or which General had a striptease artiste as his mistress... So, all these fascinating stories amply made up for the cheese-pairing.

Anyway, that is how, in spite of the generation gap between us, Mr Rona and I became 'chums'. Gradually, I felt, he was getting to trust me; and we became 'business partners' in a small racket he devised.

This involved auctioning at Sotheby's, handwritten and illuminated antique Korans, picked up at bargain basement prices at Istanbul's flee market. Mind you, Mr Rona knew his stuff. He could look at a Koran, written in 17th Century and, at a glance, recognise the hand of its calligrapher. With illuminations, pictures alongside the pages, these Korans were, in reality, pieces of art; and, in spite of not being able to read Arabic alphabet, I could not help admiring them. When I held these beautifully leather bound books in my hands, I felt I was holding history. Still, Mr Rona had a golden rule: He would never pay a cent more than $100 per Koran.

So, once the Korans were purchased, we had to activate the 'Phase II' of our operation. That is, putting them up for auction at Sotheby's – and that is where I came in.

The truth of the matter was, being the chief editor of a major newspaper, Mr Rona was quite paranoid about being seen peddling Korans at Sotheby's. So, they had to be auctioned under a different name. Only, on that occasion, 'Marcel Plume' did not quite do the trick. So, that is how I became his Trojan Horse for these transactions. Naturally, for my services, Mr Rona kindly cut me into the deal – a neat 20% on the hammer price of each item. Frankly, landing my name to a transaction which was totally legal, for 20% of the proceeds, was not a bad deal at all.

The first Koran went for £700, which meant my 20% came to £140. This may not sound like a lot of money but, given, in 1971 the annual salary of Edward Heath, the British Prime Minister, was £9,500, you can see the significance of £140, especially for a first year student at UCL.

Anyway, as our operation continued successfully, Mr Rona's visits to London became more and more frequent – of course, each time with a Koran neatly tucked in the deeper recesses of his suitcase. On average, each item sold between £700-800, and within weeks a Sotheby's cheque would arrive at my address, drawn on my name, and all I had to do was to bank it in my account.

Then came Phase III. That is, once the cheque cleared, communicating the news to Mr Rona, with the amount received. Although, in theory, this should have been a most simple task – requiring a simple telephone call, in practise it presented certain problems. Namely, due to Mr Rona's high profile job, all conversation on the phone had to be carried out in code. For example, under no circumstances was I to refer to 'Sothebys', nor utter the word 'Koran', or mention any money exchanging hands.

Mr Rona was absolutely convinced that, being the chief editor of a major daily, as a routine, Turkish Secret Service were tapping his phone. Of course, in 1970s Turkey, this was indeed more than likely. Consequently, a method of communication had to be devised to elude the prying ears of the Turkish Secret Service.

In the absence of an Enigma Machine, our code consisted of a scenario which Mr Rado himself had devised. Each time I received a cheque, I would call Istanbul and pretend I had purchased some clothing material. So, our conversations went along the following lines,

'I've got the Highland tweed you wanted.'

'How many meters?'

'800 meters.'

'Very good.'

For some reason, the absurdity of someone purchasing 800 meters of Highland Tweed never occurred to Mr Rona. What was the end use of miles of material?

More to the point, I wondered what would the Turkish Secret Service would make of these strange conversations – repeated with certain frequency. In fact, they could easily conclude, these calls had a more sinister purpose than merely peddling Korans at Sotheby's, as in Mr Rona being a Soviet Agent. After all, those days, at the height of the Cold War, Turkey was of enormous strategic importance to the Russians.

Be it as it may, not to rock the apple cart, I did go along with this charade. So, every couple of months, Mr Rona turned up in London with a few Korans neatly tucked into his suitcase, and the operation continued.

On one of those occasions, the Koran Mr Rona bought looked quite special. The illuminations were so beautifully drawn, I felt this was truly a piece of art. In fact, Mr Rona confided, for this particular volume he had broken his $100 rule and paid $150, adding:

'I was probably duped.'

Consequently, breaking another rule, he wanted to come with me, in order be present at the evaluation of the item. Given Mr Rona was paranoid about keeping his anonymity, he had never actually stepped inside Sotheby's – this was another first for him. Be that as it may, the next day we turned up at Bond Street for the appraisal.

I used to find the inner machinations of Sotheby's fascinating. It was 'Old England' par excellence – expertise, cunning, courtesy and discretion.

Appraisal meant, when a new Koran arrived, it had to be valued in order to establish a 'Reserve Price' – below which it could not be sold. What always amazed me was the vast knowledge of these experts. Old Etonians, later Oxbridge graduates, they were consummate Orientalist – each a potential Lawrence of Arabia, fluent in Arabic. Now I could see the meaning of the old adage, the British Empire was built on the playing fields of Eton.

Moreover, with the Old Etonians, Mr Rona had met his match. The boys could easily challenge him about the identity of any calligrapher by merely glancing at the style. A little ornament here, a little tail there, the boys immediately would spot the hand of the Calligrapher.

Indeed, that visit of ours was a case in point. As it happened, there was some controversy about the provenance of the Koran in question. Mr Rado argued, it was the hand of a famous 17th Century Calligrapher; whereas the Old Etonians argued, it was the hand of another, who lived in the late 16th Century. Be it as it may, finally a reserve price of £900 was agreed, and the item was enlisted for the forthcoming auction.

The next day Mr Rona left for Istanbul. However, before leaving, at the airport, I was once more warned, when talking on the phone, never to deviate from conversing in code.

Given, at the time, I was chasing an attractive second year anthropology student at UCL, I soon forgot all about the auction. Therefore, you can imagine my shock when the usual envelope from Sotheby's turned up in the post – in it with a cheque for £16,700!

Naturally, my first reaction was to assume it was a typo – that is, they had put in one zero too many. However, another shock awaited me. When I called Sotheby's in order to alert them to their error, the Sloane Ranger on the phone confirmed,

'£16,700 is the correct amount.' Noticing my silence, she added, 'It went to a Middle Eastern gentleman.'

Still in disbelief, I banked the cheque, to make sure it was not all one silly mistake. What do you know, a few days later, the cheque cleared. I had £16,700 sitting in my bank account! I even noticed a change of tone in my bank manager, when he was talking to me. Anyway, now all I had to do was to call Mr Rona, and break the news to him.

However, those days, in the early 1970s, calling Istanbul from London was no simple feast. You had to book the call the night before and, if lucky, you might be connected the next morning. In the event, I had Mr Rona at the other end of the line, just a few minutes after 8 am London time. After the polite preliminaries, I broached the matter in hand, as instructed:

'I bought the Harris Tweed you wanted.' Trying to sound casual, he asked,

'How many meters?'

'16,700 meters.'

'Come again?'

'16,700 meters.'

'My boy, be serious. How many meters?'

I yelled into the receiver: '16,700 meters. The Harris Tweed… Remember?'

'What *are* you talking about?'

By then, getting fed up with this totally absurd conversation, I yelled into the receiver:

'Sixteen thousand seven hundred Pounds Sterling!' Mr Rona yelled back,

'Shut up!' He whispered,

'I'll be there tomorrow.'

He was as good as his word. The next day, he was on the first flight from Istanbul. When I went to Heathrow to meet him, as soon as he came out of Customs and Immigration, he shrieked:

'How much?'

'£16,700!'

With that, he put his arms around me and started kissing me in all over my face. Indeed, people around us, startled, were giving us strange looks.

While we were travelling into town, along the motorway, Mr Rona asked the cab driver to take us straight to the bank. There, with his suitcase by his side, as he was counting the proceeds in hard cash, the reality finally sunk in – that this was not an elaborate joke on my part.

However, then something even stranger happened. As he placed 'the loot', (minus my 20%) in his briefcase, his hands still shaking, Mr Rona said,

'We better stop now.'

Looking back on it, I still can see in my mind's eyes, the absolutely terrified look on Mr Roma's face. I imagine, he wanted to leave the game while still on top, before ending up in a Turkish prison, in view of our cryptic exchanges on the phone, on charges of espionage.

GABRIELLE

She had long blond hair which ran down to her waist. In fact, when she kneeled down in prayer, a few pews in front of me, at the Brompton Oratory – the Catholic cathedral in London's fashionable Knightsbridge, her hair almost touched the floor.

Often she would remain in that position, deep in prayer, well after the Service had ended and the congregation was gone. This meant, we would virtually be the only people left in the cathedral – she on her knees praying and I, a few pews behind, furtively admiring her beauty.

She was tall, easily six foot, slender and looked in her mid twenties. She had a well defined face with strong features, a long nose and shapely lips. She wore no make-up, except some eyeshadow – which emphasised her enormous cobalt blue eyes.

I had often watched her walk up the isle, just like a model on a cat-walk, to take communion. She always wore low heels and a short skirt, exhibiting generously her interminably long shapely legs. Having reached the Chancel, she would kneel, let the priest place the tablet in her mouth, then walk down the isle, back to her seat. Then, she would kneel again, letting her gorgeous long mane hang behind the pew as she continued with her prayer.

Finally, the congregation having left ages ago, she would get up, take her Bible – she never used one provided by the church, and leave her pew. As she passed me by, placing my face between my hands, I used to pretend to be deep in prayer. Although, I doubt that she even noticed I existed.

Then, when I thought she had done enough praying to last her the week, she would start doing the rounds of the Saints, going from one corner to the other, lighting votive candles for every single one of them. Given the Oratory was a massive edifice and housed a fair number of Saints, that tour lasted almost an hour – as she also said a quick prayer at each port of call. It was only after the tour came full circle, she would finally leave the Cathedral.

From that point on, counting the days, I had to wait until the following Sunday, so that I could rush back to the Oratory.

This might be a good moment to say a few words about myself and, more to the point, what used to take me to the Brompton Oratory. I say 'more to the point' because, being Turkish, one is not normally associated with the Catholic Church, for that matter, with any other church.

However, those days, I was working as an assistant stage director at the Royal Opera House and, music being my passion, I was going through a period listening to organ music. So, with its superb organist and extensive repertoire of Bach Toccatas and Fugues, the Brompton Oratory became my very own concert hall. Thrown into the bargain, the Oratory had also a choir with exquisite soloists, recruited from the students of Royal College of Music – just up the road from the cathedral. The Vespers were a special treat. Indeed, I still remember a beautiful rendition of Rossini's 'La Petite Messe Solennelle'. So, the Oratory being a short walk from Belgravia where I lived, attending the service became an agreeable way to spend Sunday mornings.

Of course, with the added bonus of the 'new love' in my life – call it an infatuation or a fascination, my visits to Sunday Mass became an absolute must. I could hardly wait for the week to pass, so that I could once more rush off to the Oratory. Indeed, as I hurriedly past Harrods, my heart pounding, I would wonder if my love would still be there.

To my relief, as I entered the Oratory, I would spot her long golden mane, among the congregation, falling behind a pew. There she was, as usual, kneeling in deep prayer. At that precise moment, many a time, I remember lifting my eyes up to the huge crucifix hanging above the Altar, and whisper,

'Thank you Lord!' Then the Mass would start.

Credo in unum Deum,
Patrem omnipoténtem;
Et in unum Dóminum Iesum Christum,
Fílium Dei Unigénitum,
Et ex Patre natum ante ómnia sæcula.
Qui propter nos hómines,
Et propter nostram salútem descéndit de cælis.
Et incarnátus est de Spíritu Sancto,
Ex María Vírgine, et homo factus est…

Often, while I listened to the Priest's prayers, my mind wondered. I used to ask myself what brought this young and attractive woman to the Oratory every Sunday? More to the point, why, long after the congregation left, did she remain there, deep in prayer?

I came up with all sorts of theories. Maybe she had a terminally ill parent. I then dismissed that, given a young woman of her age could not possibly have a dying father or mother. On the other hand, when choosing its victims, cancer had no prejudices. In fact, the dying relative could easily be a brother or a sister…

For some reason however, neither the theory of dying parents, or siblings, made any sense to me. The utter abandon with which she prayed made me think the reason for such religious fervour cut much deeper. Still, what was that reason?

As I debated all the permutations, the Mass would be over. Although, now in a deserted cathedral, with her hands clasped together, she would carry on praying for an eternity.

It was on one of those occasions, a thought occurred to me. What if the terminally ill parent finally passed away and, consequently, she stopped coming to the Church? I would never see her again!

At that moment, as those notions raced through my mind, my eyes caught her Bible, left open, on the side of her pew. Suddenly, as if my movements were now dictated by Divine power, I put my hand in my pocket, fished out a pen and scribbled at the back of the Prayer Sheet, my phone number and my name, adding 'please call!'

Then, with a slight of hand, I placed the small Prayer Sheet, in the open pages of her Bible, between the Corinthians and Galatians. After that, I swiftly got up and, like a felon leaving the crime scene, I tiptoed out of the cathedral as fast as I could. Although elated, I was feeling as if I had committed a Cardinal Sin.

That week, at Covent Garden, we were rehearsing Tosca, which developed problems. The tenor, originally engaged to sing Cavaradossi, developed a throat infection and, so far, no substitute could be found. Consequently, with everybody at panic stations, the transgression I had committed at the Oratory had slipped my mind. So, you can well imagine my utter surprise when, one evening, my phone rang and the voice at the other end said,

'Hi, my name is Gabrielle. I found your note in my Bible.'

She spoke with a posh, Sloane Ranger accent. Trying desperately to keep my composure, I replied,

'How kind of you to call…'

Then, she caught me totally unawares:

'Are you a devout Catholic?'

What was I supposed to say? 'No, I am not a Catholic, devout or otherwise. In fact, I am not even a Christian. As a matter of fact, I don't believe in God.' I eventually answered—

'Naturally.'

'I thought so' she purred into the phone, adding,

'I think, I know who you are…'

After all, she had noticed I existed! She continued,

'I saw you, praying.'

'Oh yes?'

Suddenly the idea of dying parents or siblings flashed through my mind. How could I ask her for a date! She once more took me by surprise.

'Would you like to meet?' I managed to answer,

'Of course…'

'I work at Sotheby's, on Bond Street, I could meet you during my break.'

'Excellent! Shall we have lunch?'

'Would love to.'

Sloane Ranger, Sotheby's… It had to be somewhere special.

'How about Claridges?', I asked, trying to sound casual.

'It's round the corner from Sotheby's. They have charming restaurant, Le Chinoiserie, by—'

'I know it well.'

I heard alarm bells ringing, but I decided to ignore them. Then she surprised me once more.

'Tomorrow?'

'Perfect. 1 pm, the Chinoiserie?'

'See you then.'

With that she rung off. I was on cloud number nine. I had taken a risk and it paid off. However, as I was calling Claridges to book a table, a thought struck me, which brutally brought me back to earth. 'What the hell do you know about Catholicism', I asked myself. What if she started talking about it? Had she not asked, 'are you a devout Catholic?'

The next port of call was Waterstones, in Piccadilly. On arrival, I explained to the girl at the main desk what I was after. She replied,

'Religion, 3rd floor.'

Interminable bookshelves had many sub-sections. Taoism, Hinduism, Sufism, Mormonism, Moslem, Buddhism, Judaism, Shinto. I had no idea there were so many religions. No wonder the world was in such turmoil. Finally, there it was, 'The Catholic Truth', a hard bound book in a glossy jacket with a photograph of the Pope on it. I was looking at the key to my beloved's heart.

I devoured the book in one night. I had to, given, in less than twelve hours I would be meeting my Sweetheart at the Claridges. Sacraments, Baptism, Penance, confession, Holy Eucharist, Body of Christ, Mystery of Virgin Birth, Resurrection… Finally, in the wee hours with the book still in my hand, I nodded off.

Gabrielle arrived punctually at 1pm. As ever sensuous, she was wearing a simple but elegant short black number, exhibiting her interminable long legs and emphasising her harvest gold long hair, let down on a free fall. As usual, she was wearing low heel shoes – a ruse to underplay her six foot height. The 'simple but elegant' image was enhanced by a pearl necklace and matching ear-rings. The finishing touch was the sensuous but discreet perfume.

'Hi, have I kept you?' she asked in her Sloane Ranger accent, totally relaxed, as if she had known me all her life.

'I just got here', I replied, my heart pounding.

'The auction ran late. We had the Degas piece, 'Déjeuner Sur l'Herbe' and everybody was bidding like mad!'

'Oh!'

'It went for twenty million dollars.'

She ordered a Cesar salad and iced tea. To look at her slender figure, obviously she watched her diet.

To get the conversation flowing, I asked, how come she ended up working at Sotheby's? She was at Cheltenham Ladies College – hence the posh accent, then she decided to study art history, so took herself off to Paris, and spent three years at the 'Beaux Arts'.

'That's where I fell in love with the Post-impressionists', she concluded, sipping her iced tea.

Her voice had a distinctive lower register, at times almost touching the lower G, which made her even more sensuous.

'What do you do?' This was my chance to impress her.

'I am a Staff Producer at the Royal Opera House.'

'What's a staff producer?'

'He is the person who revives *other* directors' productions, when they are brought back, in later seasons.

'Other directors?'

It was time to change the subject. After all, what I really wanted to know was what brought her to the Brompton Oratory every Sunday, to pray for hours on end. The image of the 'terminally ill father' kept flashing in my mind.

'Do you believe in the healing power of prayer?' I asked, artfully. Now she would have to reveal what all that praying was in the aid of.

'It makes me feel better', she replied, toying with her Cesar Salad. So much for the dying father. Still, I persevered.

'Is your father also in the arts?' She smiled,

'He's the CEO of Lazard Frères.'

That was that. Obviously, there was not a damned thing wrong with the man. Moving away from Divinity, I asked,

'You must be quite close to him?'

'I love him to bits.' I made one last effort,

'What about your... mother?'

'Oh, she left Daddy when I was nine. She married a Greek ship owner.'

Obviously it was time to dump the theory of terminally ill parents. Evidently, the girl was religious by nature. Now, it was her turn to quiz me. Slightly embarrassed, she asked,

'If you're Turkish, how come you are a Catholic?'

'My mother... She is French.' I lied, thinking, the first time in my life, my French Lycée education paid off. Probably to test me, she asked,

'What do you think of the Confessional?'

There I had no problem. Thanks to the book I just had purchased, with the Pope's picture on the cover, I had done my homework.

'It only works, if you truly repent.'

That, obviously, was the correct answer. I could feel her cobalt blue eyes looking at me approvingly.

'I did notice you at the Oratory.'

Yet, I had assumed she did not know I even existed! There was more to come.

'I thought you were quite dishy.'

I could hardly believe my ears! Obviously, my gamble, as in slipping that 'love note' into her Bible, had paid off – now promising bigger dividends to come. Still, I tried to keep my composure. As I was trying to figure out how to react, the waiter appeared,

'Would you like some dessert?'

At that, Gabrielle glimpsed at her watch and yelped,

'My God, is that the time!', announcing that she had to run back to Sotheby's.

'Have to process the twenty million dollar.'

We skipped dessert and coffee, I paid the bill and soon we were out in the street. Just to be with her for few minutes more, I walked her to Sotheby's. As we were parting, she gave a peck on the cheek. I whispered,

'Will I see you again?'

'Why don't you call me?'

With that she slipped back into her world of Post-Impressionists, in order to process the $20 millions for 'Déjeuner Sur l'Hèrbe'.

As I headed back to Covent Garden, in order to supervise the evening's performance of Tosca. The new tenor singing Cavaradossi, who was just flown in from La Scala, announced he could 'only die on stage left'. Consequently, he needed to be walked through his movements. In reality, I could not care less about what side of the stage he got shot by the firing squad. I was on cloud number nine, and for all I cared, he could jump off the stage into the orchestra pit.

Not to appear too zealous, I gave it a few days, before calling Sotheby's. I was thinking, maybe I could invite her to the first night of Tosca.

'Sotheby's, can I help you', answered another Sloane Ranger.

'Gabrielle Nicholas, please.'

After a few seconds, I was connected to another extension.

'Post Impressionists.'

'Gabrielle, please.'

'Who should I say?'

I gave her my name and waited. A few seconds later the Sloane Ranger returned,

'Gabrielle is in a meeting, could she call you back?'

'Of course.'

By the end of the day, there was no call. I was surprised, but tried not to make too much of it. She probably was processing another multi-million dollar sale. However, by the end of the second day, when my call was still not returned, I called Sotheby's again. After going through the same routine, the posh voice at the other end announced,

'Gabrielle is in a meeting.'

I decided to give it a few more days, and tried once more. This time, however, as I was dialling Sotheby's number, I had a premonition of impending doom.

'Who should I say is calling?' Following the same routine, the girl came back,

'She's in a meeting.'

In the evening, we had another performance of Tosca, for which I had laid my hands on two House Seats, thinking I would take Gabrielle to it, which I returned. The performance went well. Remembering his movements, the new tenor even managed to die at correct side of the stage. At the end of the performance, he took nine curtain calls.

After the performance, I decided to walk home, from Covent Garden to Belgravia. It was a damp November evening, and people carrying umbrellas kept passing me by. It was only that fact which finally made me realise it was raining, and I had no umbrella. By then I had reached the Ritz and there, suddenly, the reality hit me: I was dumped.

I spent the next few months analysing. We had a pleasant lunch – at a classy restaurant. We chatted a bit, flirted a bit. Did she not say she found me 'quite dishy'? So, where had I gone wrong?

Finally, not to make myself ill, I drew a line under the whole episode. I swept my hurt under the carpet, philosophising women were mysterious creatures. After all, was it not Sigmund Freud who said, after forty years of psychoanalysis, he still did not understand them. So, who was I next to the great Viennese professor, to solve the mysteries of the female psyche?

* * *

A few years elapsed and, by then, I was working at the New York City Opera, still as a Staff Producer – reviving other directors' work. I also had convinced myself, probably thanks to living on a different continent, that Gabrielle had been nothing more than a flash in the pan – a silly infatuation. I had spoken too soon.

One day, having a bit of a tooth ache, I ended up at the surgery of a New York dentist, just behind the Lincoln Center. As I was in the anteroom, waiting for my turn, I picked up copy of Vanity Fair. Suddenly, a full page photograph hit me. There she was, Gabrielle, in a slinky summer dress, with a man in her arm, in his late forties, in Bermuda shorts and a t-shirt. The caption read, 'Gabrielle Holden, née Armstrong, the Queen Bee of International Jet Set, and her husband Donald Holden, on their private Caribbean island, Le Monocle'.

There was also a short paragraph about the husband, 'the most successful Hedge Fund manager on Wall Street' – Private jets, yachts, polo courses, race horses; properties in Sutton Place, Long Island, Eton Square, Avenue Hoche, Verbier, and Monte Carlo – the works. Net worth, $33 billion.

Suddenly, the shroud of mystery about the interminable prayers, votive candles, Holy Communion was lifted. Neither was there a dying father, nor mother, or siblings either. The truth was much simpler, and it was staring at me on the pages of Vanity Fair. Suddenly, I felt purged of all torment of unrequited love.

'The dentist will see you now,' the nurse called out.

I placed the Vanity Fair back on the table, where I had found it – for other patients to browse through, and headed for the dentist's chair.

AMSTERDAM

When I was in my teens, Amsterdam held a great fascination for me. Looking back, it probably had something to do with a French movie I saw when I was a boy in Istanbul. It was called 'La Fille Dans La Vitrine', ('Girl in the Window'), with a 1960s French movie star, Marina Vlady, a most attractive blond with beautiful green eyes. The moment I saw her on the silver screen, I developed a desperate school boy crush on her.

However, there was another reason why that film had made such an impression on me. Marina Vlady played a prostitute who marketed her services by sitting in a shop window, along the canal in Amsterdam – That was the start of my fascination about that city. Still, it was not until I was twenty-one that I were to visit Amsterdam for real.

The series of events which led me to Amsterdam started on a Saturday evening with the persistent ringing of my door bell, as if it was a matter of life and death.

By then, I had been living in London for eight years. Now, having left the French Lycée, I was in my second year at UCL, reading International Law, with a view to joining the Turkish Ministry of Foreign Affairs – a prospect which filled me with little enthusiasm.

To revert to our story, the unexpected visitor was no other than one Cengiz Tura, a Turkish friend of mine. We had arrived in London more or less the same time – in the early sixties.

Cengiz was everything that I was not. He loved partying, clubbing, dancing, as if he was born for the Swinging Sixties. A year older than I, 22, quite tall, he was the spitting image of a singing icon of the times – Tom Jones. In fact, due to his 'Afro' hair, and the way he moved to music, I was sure, way back, Cengiz had some Afro genes.

Anyway, Afro or not, he had great success with the opposite sex; almost every night, ending up with a different one to take home. In fact, he used to brag, if he slept with the same girl twice, it would mean he was losing his 'Mojo'.

Whereas, I would bend backwards in order to hang on to the same girl as long as I could. I was shy, bookish and socially clumsy. In music, I liked Beethoven, Mozart and opera. Worse still, I had a strong distaste of pop music. Whereas, as everyone knows, if you wanted to have any success with the opposite sex, Fidelio or Tristan hardly prepared you for the disco floor. No wonder, in that department, I was a total failure. Whereas Cengiz had rhythm flowing throughout his body.

Of course, that sort of activity required certain props. Luckily, Cengiz's Daddy had provided him with a slender, jet red, E Type Jaguar. Another must was a trendy address – in this case, a mews house in London's fashionable Knightsbridge, discreetly tucked away behind Harrods. There, Cengiz entertained into the wee hours, sewing his wild oats.

Cengiz's father was a professor of Economics at University of Istanbul. Of course, you might wonder, how come the meagre salary of an academic, in 1970s Turkey, would suffice to fund the profligate lifestyle of the prodigal son. The truth was, Tura senior also sat at the boards of various conglomerates – a bank, a shipping company, a media group, plus a few other big concerns. In fact, at one time, he had even been the chief economic advisor to a Prime Minister of Turkey, who, following a military Coup, sadly ended up in the scaffold.

The odd thing about Cengiz's father, an intelligent man by all accounts, was his being in denial about his son's true nature. In fact, he hoped, like himself, Cengiz would end up in Academia. To this end, using his influence, he even had secured him a place at the Ivy League Williams College in Boston Massachusetts – with a scholarship!

Only, Cengiz lasted there just over three weeks. Then, one Saturday night, placing his passport in his pocket and, in the clothes he was standing in, he headed for the Boston airport, where he bought himself a one way ticket on the first available flight to London. So, the partying continued.

I must admit that secretly, I admired his ability to make decisions on an impulse, and act upon them instantly. In fact, in later life, putting his passport in his pocket and heading for the nearest airport – sometimes not even knowing where he was going, became a trademark of his.

That is, more or less, how our Amsterdam trip started. As I was saying, it was a Saturday night, I was watching television, and my door bell started ringing incessantly. As soon as Cengiz stepped into my flat, he announced:

'I wanna get laid. Let's go clubbing!'

Since I had no pressing engagements, I readily accepted the proposal. To be fair, whatever character flaws Cengiz might have, stinginess was not one of them. When you were in his company, he would never let you put your hand into your pocket – not even to buy him the odd drink.

Anyway, as we came out of my flat, I noticed, his jet red E Type was not there. He explained, he had taken it to be serviced, and since he did not wish to be 'carless', he had rented a Mini Cooper, which I could now see, was parked right in front of the house I lived in.

As we drove along Park Lane, Cengiz kept singing 'I can't get no satisfaction', a Rolling Stones hit of 1960s.

'What are we celebrating?' I asked.

'Look in the glove compartment', he replied, with a grin. When I did, I found an envelope.

'What is it?'

'Just read it.'

When I opened the envelope, out came a Medical certificate, written on a hospital stationary, duly signed by a consultant psychiatrist, with many letters after his name. The gist of it was, in advanced stages of schizophrenia, Cengiz was unfit for Military Service.

'The shrink was expensive, but worth every penny', he said, as we turned into Berkeley Square. 'The beauty of it is that nobody can prove him wrong.'

'In your case, they don't have to', I answered.

'You see, being a looney is not a kinda thing that shows on X-rays.'

Now it was clear, we were celebrating Cengiz wiggling his way out the military service – those days a neat twenty-six months!

As we stepped into The Revolution, in 1970s a trendy club off Berkeley Square, it's dimly lit atmosphere, red velvet walls, the smell of cigarettes blending with whisky and perfume, I forgot the outside world. Ordering our drinks, Cengiz reiterated,

'Tonight's the night!'

The club was buzzing with attractive women – eyeing us up as much we were eyeing them. Soon enough, we were joined by two enticing brunettes. It must have been my lucky night, as one of them turned out to be a philosophy student at the Sorbonne – a Godsend for a shy, but French speaking bookworm, such as myself.

The philosopher and I hit it off immediately – a rare phenomenon, given, in natural order of things, it was always Cengiz who was 'the star attraction'. As I was thinking, 'Every dog has its day', Cengiz said – speaking in Turkish,

'These broads are boring, let's get outta here.'

'My one is a student at the Sorbonne', I protested.

'Who gives a shit!'

Before I could utter another word, Cengiz sprung to his feet and said to the girls,

'See ya…'

When Cengiz was in a spot, he always 'became' American. Within minutes we were back in the rented Mini Cooper, driving along Green Park.

'So much for getting laid', I quipped.

'Plenty more where those came from…'

Well, the night belonged to him. After all, he was celebrating wiggling his way out of the Turkish Military. Moreover, knowing him, unless the festivities resulted in spending untold sums of money, commensurate with the matter in hand, they would totally be devoid of any meaning. Only, what that ratio was going to be, I was yet to discover.

I do not wish to bore you with details of what happened at our next port of call, La Valbonne, another trendy club in 1970s London; suffice it to say it was a repeat performance of what took place at The Revolution. Girls were offering themselves on a plate, but invariably, Cengiz wanted to 'move on'.

Things did not get any better at Bag O' Nails, or Speakeasy. By now, we had walked out on a considerable number of most enticing girls and 'moved on'. While driving, in between clubs, Cengiz reassured me:

'The night is young…' Finally, I put my foot down:

'It's fucking 3 am, and I'm going home!'

'Don't be a wimp!'

'Drop me at Lowndes Square, or I'll take a cab!'

Sensing, unless he came up with a hugely original idea and, by now, 'getting laid' was not one of them, I was no longer going to play ball. Once more in American, Cengiz yelped:

'Hey Man, let's go to Amsterdam!'

'Are you *totally* deranged?' I yelled.

'I heard about this Canal Street, with the women in shop windows…'

Suddenly 'La Fille Dans La Vitrine', the movie starring Marina Vlady flashed in my mind. I answered,

'Let's do it!'

No sooner I said it, I knew I was making a colossal mistake. With relish, Cengiz responded:

'Now you're talking like a man!'

Quickly, we stopped by our respective homes – literally, just to pick up our passports and a toothbrush, and we were on our way.

By the time we arrived in Dover it was 6 am. Given that it was January, it was still pitch black outside. However, we were in luck, the next ferry to Ostend was about to depart.

Once we set sail, with the Mini Cooper safely in the haul, we went onto the upper deck – where the freezing sea air and the wind woke me up:

'By the way, I don't have a bean', I announced.

'I got tons…'

I knew, due to his impulsive nature, Cengiz always carried on his person large sums of cash.

On the English Channel in pitch dark, apart from a few flickering lights emanating from vessels sailing in the distance, there was no sign of life whatsoever. Contemplating the vast space in from of me, I wondered what had possessed me to say 'yes' to this crazy expedition.

By the time we disembarked, at Ostend, it was daylight. Soon we were driving along a Belgian motorway, towards Holland.

After eight hours driving, broken up by sandwiches and coffee at an autoroute canteen, we finally entered a totally snowed under Holland. Now driving at a tortoise speed, by the time we made it to Amsterdam it was early evening.

Wherever in the world, finding a hotel had never posed a problem to Cengiz. He would just pick up a five start establishment, and walk in as if he owned the place. In this case, it happened to be the Amsterdam Hilton.

Happily, those days, in the absence of Visa cards, you could walk into any five-star hotel, show your passport and the receptionist would simply hand over the key to your room. Unlike today, demanding upfront payment was unheard of – and considered totally unseemly. Moreover, once checked in, you could use all the facilities of the hotel – the room service, restaurants, bars etc.to your heart's content. When presented a bill, all you had to do was put down your room number and scribble a signature. Of course, for Cengiz, that was a red rag to the bull. In the event, we took two superior suites.

When I checked into my suite, and hopped into the shower to freshen up, suddenly, the absurdity of the whole situation hit me. Twenty-four hours ago I was peacefully watching TV at home in London; now, skipping sleep, and having driven hundreds of miles, I was in Amsterdam. All this because of a French movie I had seen when I was a boy, about a woman in a window!

* * *

The dinner consisted of Chateaubriand washed down with Lynch-Château Lynch-Bages 1953, which Cengiz had picked up at the recommendation of the Sommelier. That was followed up with Crêpes

Suzettes flambés, washed down with Remy Martin XO. Now, our spirits restored, I suggested,

'I suppose, we might take a stroll along the Canal Street…'

'Canal Street?'

'The girls in the windows…'

'Hey, I never paid for it in my life, and I certainly ain't gonna start now!' Cengiz answered, once more in American.

'Wasn't that the whole purpose of this expedition?'

Not taking the slightest notice, he pushed in front of me the Menu, advertising a night club, 007, at the top floor of the Hilton.

'Let's go check it out.'

007 was a dimly lit small disco, at the roof of the Hilton, with panoramic views of Amsterdam – now quite picturesque with pelting snow. The DJ was playing the ABBA song, *Money, Money, Money, it's a rich man's world…*

To my surprise, at 007, there were hardly any men – but the place was full of women, mostly blondes, scattered around the place. Cengiz remarked,

'What did I tell you.'

As we settled down to our seats, realising a couple sexy blondes eyeing us, I said,

'We might get lucky with those.'

Thereupon, Cengiz beckoned the waiter and instructed him to take over a bottle of Bollinger to the girls. Soon, raising their glasses, they invited us to join them. The blondes spoke perfect English. One of them, an interpreter at the International Court of Justice, seem to take a shine to me. However, Cengiz suddenly spoke in Turkish:

'Man, these broads are boring, let's move on.'

Before I could get a word in edgeways, he sprung to his feet and once more in American, spoke to the girls,

'See ya, babe.'

'That was a bottle of Bollinger down the drain', I commented.

Of course, this was a red rag to the bull. Within minutes a new bottle was sent over to another table. To cut a long story short, the next couple of hours were spent, with countless bottles of Bollinger travelling to various tables. Then, we would be invited to join the girls; however in no time, with a quick 'See ya', Cengiz would move on.

I reckoned, at 007, we ran up a bill for at least half a dozen bottles of Special Cuvée Bollinger. When the bill was presented, without flinching, Cengiz scribbled his room number and signed it, while leaving a bundle of bank notes as tip. By now, I was pondering what exactly was the purpose of this kamikaze mission.

'So much for getting laid', I commented.

'This place sucks, let's go somewhere else.'

'Are you *totally* insane!' I finally exploded. 'I haven't slept for twenty-four hours, I'm beat!' Totally calm, Cengiz replied,

'The night is young.'

'It's 2 fucking am in the morning!' I shrieked, 'You have been trying to get laid since Saturday evening – now it's almost Monday morning!

'Hey Man, just cool it' was the response.

It was the Concierge who gave us the name of a club – the only establishment open in Amsterdam, for Jazz enthusiasts, at this late hour, or early morning.

A cab was summoned, and we were on our way. By now, Amsterdam was totally snowed-under, more of it pelting down in huge flakes. Cengiz kept humming the old Rolling Stones song, 'I can't get no satisfaction', while accompanying himself by tapping on the frozen window of the cab.

The new venue, 'Blue Note', was a jazz club and, certainly, no

73

Bollinger-land. It was buzzing with hippies, druggies, drop-outs and such like. A small ensemble was performing some jazz – totally unintelligible for one whose musical taste stopped in XIX century.

In the air, I could sniff some sweet substance – which had recently been legalised in Holland. Making full use of this fact, I realised, the clientele were totally stoned.

Realising that he had been taken out of his middle-class comfort zone and that this was one place where splashing his cash would not cut any ice, Cengiz suddenly became irritable:

'All communists!'

As I was hoping for the proverbial, 'Man, let's get outta here', two hippy type women invited themselves to our table. Although in t-shirts, with short hair and no make-up, in their own way, they were quite attractive. One of them, with beautiful green eyes, was a CND activist; the other described herself as a Marxist existentialist poet. Smoking joints, they were already on cloud number nine.

Cengiz got drinks all around. However, I do not know if it was due to the amount of dope in the air which I was inhaling, or the events of the last twenty-four hours, I simply nodded off.

The next thing I remember was Cengiz shaking me forcefully.

'The broads like us – even *you*! How can you score if you nod off?', he said, in Turkish. That was the last straw:

'Fuck scoring, fuck getting laid and fuck screwing! I'm off!'

With that I sprung to my feet and headed for the exit. I could hear Cengiz shouting after me:

'I'll bring them to the hotel. Order some champagne from the room service.'

I did not bother answering. I was past coherent talk.

When I got out of 'Blue Note' it was snowing in big flakes, and the temperature was about -20°C. Not surprisingly, there was no cab to be seen. Mercifully, a Karl Marx look alike, walking into the club, pointed me in the direction of a cab rank. As I walked on, due to freezing cold air, I started waking up. In fact, by the time I got to the cab rank, I was decidedly perky.

I told the driver to take me to the Hilton. Due to snow, as we were driving at tortoise speed, the driver started up a conversation.

'First time in Amsterdam?'

'Yes.'

'Ever heard of Canal Street?'

Had I ever heard of it... How could explain, at this ungodly hour, about 'The Girl in the Window', starring Marina Vlady?

'Never heard of it.' I answered, hoping to cut off the conversation. However, he was not the type to take 'no' for an answer.

'It's very interesting, one day you must try...'

I don't know what possessed me, suddenly I told him,

'Let's go!' Puzzled, he replied,

'I didn't mean *now*.'

'It has to be now, I'm leaving in the morning', I lied.

The taxi dropped me at the corner of a narrow street. On one side, there was a string of small houses, on the other, a frozen canal. I paid the driver. As he was about to drive off, he stuck his head out of the window,

'Good luck.'

I stood by the Canal Street, taking in the scene in front of me. It was as if the fifteen year old boy, at an Istanbul cinema, was mysteriously lifted off his seat, and pushed into the magic world of the silver screen.

So, in this no man's land, between fact and fiction, there I was, standing in my blazer, with snow pelting down, in -20°C. I started strolling along the Canal, in search of 'La Fille dans la Vitrine'. The place looked exactly like in the movie – a string of small houses, all in different colours, looking like Dolls Houses – each with a large window. Only, now, all the curtains were drawn, and there was no Marina Vlady.

Suddenly, I noticed a light reflecting off a block of ice on the canal. Surely, it must have originated from a 'Doll's House'. I was right. There it was, behind a window, an attractive blond in a silky negligée, sitting at an arm chair with her shapely legs crossed, reading a book. Almost feeling guilty to interrupt, I gingerly rung the door bell. She put her book down, got up and opened the door.

I left her after half an hour. Now I was back, on the Canal Street. Only, this time, 5 am in the morning, in -20°C, and a frozen canal on my left, standing in a light blazer, I was very much in the real world – about to freeze to death. Lifting up the lapels of my jacket, I started walking down under the pelting snow, hoping, by miracle, to find a taxi.

At that moment, a curious phenomenon occurred. I spotted a figure, like a dot against the white, snowed down, landscape, moving in my direction. What do you know, as we got closer, the dot turned out to be no other than Cengiz. When we eventually met, before I could utter one word, he beat me to it,

'All bloody lesbians!'

'And what brings you here?'

'Look who's talking.'

'I got laid. That was the whole idea, remember?'

'Great! Where do I go?'

'I thought you never paid for it.'

'Fuck you too!'

'I'm good, thank you.' Now, he changed his tactics.

'What's she like?'

I told him, after me, she probably had closed shop.

'You were that good, Ha?' I yelped:

'For fuck's sake, you're not going to screw the same girl! What do you expect me to do, give an introduction!'.

'You two are serious, or something?'

I wondered if Cengiz saw the absurdity of two men at 5 am, standing outside in -20°C snowy weather, wearing light jackets, in a strange city, arguing about a hooker.

Realising, if we continued, we would soon freeze to death, and hoping maybe she could call us a cab, I relented,

'Come, I'll take you to her.'

'Hurry up, I'm feeling horny!'

Luckily, my Marina Vlady was behind her window, exactly as before – reading her book. I rung the door-bell and, as if a re-play, she placed a book mark in her tome, got up and opened the door.

While I was dithering to explain what Cengiz was after, she asked if we would care to have a 'threesome'. I declined, on grounds of being jaded. Still, she did make me a cup of tea, before taking Cengiz in.

Hardly had I time to finish my tea, the girl re-appeared. Noticing the expression on her face, I felt, things had not quite run as planned.

'Take your friend and go!', she ordered. Still, she did, kindly, call us a cab.

By then, it was almost 7 am, and being Monday, through the window of the cab, under pelting snow, I could see people going to work – some walking in heavy coats and fur hats; others, at a bus stop, waiting for public transport...

When we finally retuned to the Hilton, the lobby was quite busy with some guests checking out. By then, Cengiz and I were hardly in talking terms. I never asked, nor wanted to know, what he had done, for that sweet natured girl to throw us out unceremoniously. As soon as I made it to my enormous suite, I crashed in the clothes I was standing in.

* * *

I woke up with the phone ringing. Naturally, it was Cengiz – in his American persona.

'Hey Man, gonna sleep all day?'

I looked at my watch, it was hardly 10 am! What was the use... I could never go back to sleep now. So, I had a quick shower and joined him at the breakfast room.

'Man, I hate this fucking town', he exclaimed, tucking into his eggs and bacon.

I could have reminded him the whole expedition was his idea, but knowing I was a willing participant, I thought better of it.

'Man, let's beat it, *now!*', he said forcefully.

What did he mean by that? We had arrived in Amsterdam by car. By now, with dozens of Bollinger offered to every woman at 007, we must have run up a colossal bill. For a start, that had to be settled. Then, we needed money to put petrol in the car, and buy tickets for the cross channel ferry.

'How much cash have you got?', I asked.

'I gave it all to the hooker.' Trying to remain calm, I said,

'Then, we must wait until your bank wires some money.'

'Fuck the bank!' He exploded, 'I wanna go back to London, now!'

'And what do you propose to use for money?'

'Hey, we got no luggage, we'll walk.' Needless to say, all these lines were delivered as James Dean, or Elvis.

Seeing my shock, to appease, he added,

'I'll wire them the money from London.'

'And how are we going to get to London? Are you going to pee in the tank for petrol!'

'We'll leave the car behind.'

'So, shall we hitch-hike?'

I wondered if he had gone clinically insane. Still, tucking into his scrambled eggs, Cengiz outlined his strategy.

Since we had no luggage, we could, literally, walk out of the hotel. Then we would pick up the car from the garage, drive to the airport, dump it at the car park, return the keys at the Avis desk, and take the next flight to London.

'And how do you propose to pay for the air fares?'

With a snigger, Cengiz took out a cheque book from his pocket and placed it on the table.

'With this.'

'How?'

'British Airways always accept cheques. Even some might bounce, what do have they to lose? It's better than having empty seats.

'It's almost criminal', I quipped.

'All high finance is criminal', he replied. Son of a professor of economics, Cengiz obviously had learnt something from his father.

'Best to fly First Class.'

'Why?'

'Not to arouse suspicion'.

By now, I was too tired to offer any opposition. If I wanted to sleep in my own bed that night, I had no choice but go along with this highly criminal plan.

We started the operation, exactly as planned. First, we walked out of the Hilton, as if going for a stroll. Then, we picked up the rented Mini Cooper from the garage, and speeded to the airport. So far, Cengiz's plan worked like a Swiss Clock. Sadly, all that changed at the airport.

While Cengiz was busy giving British Airways his dud cheque, I went to Avis desk, in order to hand over the key to the Mini Cooper. However, when the girl saw the tag on the key, she almost had a fit. The car had been reported missing. Also, those days cars were not rented on a 'Free Mileage' basis. So, one could imagine how much we had clocked up, from London to Amsterdam.

As the girl was making frantic phone calls, in Dutch – to the police, I assumed, I quietly sneaked away from the Avis desk. What else could I do?

Finally, we were airborne. Soon, at the safety of thirty thousand feet, sipping champagne and tucking into foie-gras, perks of first class travel, I could pretend the whole thing was a bad dream.

So… This was how I ended up visiting Amsterdam – as the result of a school boy crush on a French movie star.

As for Cengiz, I have no idea if he ever paid the Amsterdam Hilton – I never asked, nor wished to know.

However, the Avis bill was another story. You may remember, the medical certificate pronouncing Cengiz a schizophrenic, in the glove compartment of the Mini Cooper. Guess what, he never received a bill from Avis. Probably they saw little point in pursuing a man who was clinically certified as being in advanced stages of schizophrenia.

These days, I hear through the grapevine that he lives in LA. Still a bachelor, I am told, he is the greatest Casanova in Tinseltown.

PERFECT TIMING

This is an odd story and, to this day, I have not quite figured out what it is about. So, I have decided to put pen to paper, in the hope that, one day, the reader might make something of it.

Azadé was my paternal uncle's ex-wife. Although she and my uncle were divorced, they still saw each other whenever they could. I say 'whenever', because uncle was with the Turkish Ministry of Foreign Affairs and those days, in early 1960s, he was serving as Turkish ambassador to Josip Broz Tito's Yugoslavia. Still, whenever in Istanbul, he used to visit his ex-wife and, more often than not, take me along with him.

At the time, in my mid-teens, I had no idea why I was included in those visits, except, I assumed, Uncle needed a 'chaperone' as a gentle reminder to his ex-wife, that these visits were purely of social nature. However, given Azadé was a most attractive, sensuous and sophisticated woman, I could not imagine why any man would want to keep these visits purely social; or, for that matter, why uncle would have divorced her, in the first place.

On the other hand, I had heard from my mother – probably the most indiscreet woman in Istanbul, that few months into their marriage, when uncle was serving as a young First Secretary at the Turkish Embassy in London, Azadé had caught him 'in flagrante' with their French Nanny, and had divorced him on the spot. Of course, being seriously rich on her own right, Azadé could easily afford to ditch her adulterous husband at a hat's drop.

Indeed as I was told, she was a princesss, from the old Ottoman dynasty. Anyway, a princess or not, as far as I was concerned, she was the most beautiful woman in the world, and that was that. With her red hair and most expressive emerald green eyes, defined by eye-brows drawn like arches, she looked like a Meissen Doll. And, thanks to her Ivory skin, she also had translucent quality. Her shapely lips, I felt, had a 'sad smile', making her all the more mysterious.

As for her voice, with its slight timbre in the lower register, it signalled an independent nature. On that score, again according to my mother, Azadé had 'quite a reputation'.

'I'll say no more…', my mother used to comment demurely.

Still, Azadé never struck me as a woman who gave two hoots about what others might think of her. All the same, probably due to her English education, Tudor Hall, no less, Azadé had a certain reserve and kept everybody at a distance.

She owned a majestic, ten bedroom, wooden mansion – referred in Turkish as a 'yali', sitting on the European shores of the Bosporus – the narrow strip of water which separates Asia from Europe. There, she lived alone, in some style, attended by a butler in white tie, and a squadron of liveried servants.

Last but not least, she had something which nobody else had in Istanbul in those days – a 1955 'Silver Dawn' Rolls Royce. On rare occasions when she ventured out, she would travel in it, running around the streets of Istanbul, driven by her chauffeur in his grey tunic, gloves, cap, boots – the works. In a city where all the good and great, the Nouveau Riche Turkish middle class, travelled in their American automobiles – Chevrolets, Buicks and Cadillacs, the 1955 Silver Dawn most certainly put Azadé a class above the rest.

When uncle and I paid a visit to Azadé, we would sit on her balcony overlooking the Bosphorus and 'take tea' – which consisted also of finger sandwiches, scones with clotted cream and jam, served by her butler. As one can imagine, to a Turkish boy in his mid-teens this simply was a world apart.

To complete the picture, occasionally she and my uncle would break into English. This, I assumed, was in order to have a few words in private. Although, Azadé never gave me the impression as if she had anything private to say to my uncle. She was sophisticated, hugely attractive, but had been let down in love. She never forgave him for that.

As for my uncle, oddly, he was quite a handsome fellow. In fact, at a certain light, he reminded me of the 1960s Hollywood actor, Cary Grant. Indeed, uncle had a studied 'Englishness'. Only, emulating the 'country squire' look – with Viyella shirts (which my mother used to call 'dish cloth'), hush puppies, beige flannel trousers, tweed jackets, and club ties, he probably went slightly over the top.

As for myself, I would quietly sip my tea, tuck into my scones with clotted cream, and furtively admire Azadé. Sometimes, she would ask me some humiliating question, such as how I was doing at school or, if my grades satisfactory. Obviously, as far as she was concerned, I was merely a boy.

However, one day, she took me by total surprise. Locking those deep emerald green eyes onto mine, she asked,

'What are you going to do with your life?'

Caught totally unawares, as I was racking my brain to think of an interesting answer to impress her, when uncle came to my rescue:

'Naturally, he will go for *the career*.'

In ambassadorial parlance, *the career* meant joining the Turkish Ministry of Foreign Affairs. After all, did I not have two uncles who were ambassadors with the Turkish Ministry of Foreign Affairs? Still, I do not think uncle's answer, volunteered on my behalf, convinced Azadé: because, ever courteous, she mused:

'I thought, he might've been better off in the arts…'

That was the last time I saw her. Few weeks later, in September 1963, I was dispatched to England to continue with my schooling, and that was that.

After the French Lycée in South Kensington, I finally ended up at UCL, University College London, reading International Relations, in order, as uncle had predicted, with a view to joining the Turkish Ministry of Foreign Affairs.

However, while at UCL, I was discovering some home truths. I noticed, for example, most of my time was spent at the Drama Society, directing plays and operas. Obviously, *the career* was not for me and, worse still , I was not for *the career*.

However, as luck would have it, soon after leaving UCL, I managed to get a foot in at the Royal Opera House. Although I was merely a 'teaboy', theatrical parlance for assistant director, in the bohemian and liberal atmosphere of Covent Garden, surrounded by drama and music, I was as happy as a lark. I had found myself. More to the point, Azadé's prophecy had come to pass.

'That ungrateful rake!' My Uncle shrieked.

According to my mother, learning I had changed horses in midstream, dropping the Diplomatic, in favour of the Arts.

However, things did not stop at that. During a summer holiday, when I was visiting my parents in Istanbul, one evening, uncle came to dinner. I do not know if this was prearranged or not but, there, he decided to lock horns with me.

84

'What's wrong with *the career*?' He enquired, somewhat raising his voice.

'There is nothing wrong with it', I replied, 'except, it just doesn't appeal to me.'

'And being a 'teaboy' does…'

'It keeps me happy.'

'Think of your family name', he insisted, 'if you play your cards right, one day you might end up as ambassador to London.'

'*You* didn't quite make it to London did you?', I retorted.

There was hush at the table. Obviously I had hit below the belt. The truth was, after being caught with his pants down with a French woman, by his wife, uncle's carrier had come to a grinding halt. Thereafter, although elevated to ambassadorial rank, his postings consisted of Soviet Block satellites such as Albania or Yugoslavia. Worse still, his brother, my second uncle, had a brilliant career with a ambassadorial postings in Bern, Moscow, and London.

The hush went on for an eternity. Then, uncle got up and addressed my mother:

'Madam, if you would excuse me…'

Upon which, he placed his napkin on the table and walked out.

'Happy now?' Burst out my father.

* * *

Years came and went, and I continued with my life at Covent Garden, and forgotten all about the incident during that fateful summer holiday, until one day, Azadé was to reappear in my life.

One day, my father was visiting London. By then, although our relationship was still frosty, we were at least on talking terms. After all, as a hard-nosed businessman, it had been a hard blow for him to accept that all the money he had poured in my education paid no dividend, as I ended up as 'a mere teaboy' at Covent Garden.

Still, on his last evening, over dinner at the Savoy Grill, my father seemed to have decided to let bygones be bygones. Indeed, he ordered a 1952 Gevrey Chambertin and we had a enjoyable time, as a father and son, just chatting away. Then, as we were having our desserts, he mentioned, on his way back to Istanbul, he would be stopping over in Zurich, as his brother – Azadé's ex, was having a 'routine' check-up, at the Kantonsspital.

The next morning, In the spirit of repairing our relationship, I drove my father to Heathrow, where he took a Swissair flight to Zurich. Still, as I was driving back from the airport, I admit, I was relieved to see the back of him. Now I was thinking what to do with my evening.

Most surprises in life start with a phone call, and this one was no exception. As I got back into my flat, I just managed to catch my phone ringing. When I picked up the receiver, the husky female voice at the other end of the line said:

'I hope you remember me…'

How could I ever forget that voice and the very special, upper class accent.

'It's Madam Azadé.' I managed to mumble.

'I am staying at Claridges. I was wondering, if you would care to join me for dinner?' Then she added coquettishly,

'*If* you are free.'

I realised now she was treating me as a grown up man – with a busy social diary.

I was about to bellow,

'Am I free!' However, I managed to control myself,

'I'd be delighted.'

'Shall we say seven, for cocktails.'

With that, she was gone. For a while I stood there, with the receiver in my hand, listening to the ringing tone. Was I dreaming? Finally I came down to earth. It was almost 5 pm. I needed to get ready!

First I had a quick shower; then, I shaved and pampered myself with cologne, sprays, deodorants and more cologne. I brushed my teeth and gargled with breath-fresheners. What was I going to wear?

As luck would have it, only a few days ago, at Harrods, I had bought a new blazer. This was the moment to test drive it. I quickly got dressed – light beige trousers, a pink Turnbull & Asser shirt, with a mauve flowery silk tie. Then, I placed a colourful pochette in the top pocket of the blazer and sprinkled another dash of Chanel 'Eau Sauvage'. Finally, I was ready to go into the night and fall in love again. I opened the door to let myself out, and it was at that precise moment, the phone rung.

My first instinct was to ignore it, given now I was totally focused on Claridges, and what the night might have in reserve for me… Still, against my better judgement, I did answer the call. That was a mistake.

It was my father, calling from Zurich. I listened to what he had to say in horror. By the time he finished, my whole world was turned upside down. This is what had happened:

As soon as he checked in at Baur Au Lac, his usual hotel in Zurich, my father went straight to the Kantonsspital where his brother was having his check up. He asked the receptionist to see him. The woman requested my father to wait a minute, while she made a phone call, speaking in Zürcher Deutsche – an impenetrable dialect of German. Soon a doctor appeared.

'May I ask, Sir, what is your relation to the patient?', he asked.

'He is my brother.'

The doctor explained. The result of the tests performed had revealed uncle had advanced Leukaemia which was terminal.

Thereafter, uncle was taken to his room where he had a massive heart attack and died.

'A blessing from God…' concluded, my father.

My hopes for a romantic evening now in tatters, I failed to see the blessing from God, or anyone else… As I put the phone down, I murmured,

'Perfect timing!'

Suddenly, I felt as if I had won a fortune at the roulette table, only, when I wanted to cash in the chips, I was told they had no value whatsoever.

By now it was well past 7 pm. I had to think fast! I had two alternatives. First, carry on with the evening, as if I knew nothing. After all, would it not be the case, if I had not answered that phone call? By now, I would be having cocktails with the woman I had worshipped from the get-go.

'Sod him!' I thought.

After all, wasn't he the man caught with his pants down, within months into his marriage? Wasn't he the man who turned my father against me, just because I refused to join the Turkish Ministry of Foreign Affairs. What did I owe him?

However, the truth was, I did answer the phone, I did learn he had a heart attack and died. And now, he was lying on a cold mortuary slab, at a hospital in Zurich. How could I possibly turn up at Claridges, and have cocktails with his wife, (ex or not), as if all was dandy!

I picked up the phone, and slowly dialled the number of Claridges. Soon I had Azadé on the line. Hearing my voice, flirtatious, she said,

'I'll be down in a minute, Darling.'

I tried to say something, but I had no voice.

'You *are* downstairs?'

'Well, that's what I was calling about…'

'Oh?'

'I won't be able to make it tonight. I'm sorry.'

There was a short silence. Then she answered,

'So am I.'

Then I heard a click, and that was that. I was listening to the dial-tone.

* * *

Over the years, I often wondered how things would have panned out, if I had played my cards differently. What if I had carried on as if I did not know what had happened?

Then, the second alternative struck me. What if, when we were in throes of passion, Azadé received a phone call revealing her ex-husband had just died; and she realised I knew it all along.

However, there is one more 'what if' which, even now, I try not to think about: What if she had heard the news *before* me?

I decided not to let it spoil her evening.

As I said, this is an odd story and I have never been able to make head or tail of it. Except, perhaps, to realise, some people have a talent for living and some don't. Azadé certainly belonged to the first category, hence her 'reputation'.

As for myself, I still have the consolation prize – the memory of that magic moment, the thrill and the frisson between the two phone calls – being invited to cocktails at Claridges…

LEYLA

For Haldun Taner

She was a brunette, with long hair, well below her shoulders, and looked about twenty-two. She had large brown eyes and a shapely figure, with legs, if slightly muscular, running forever. I met her in Istanbul, by accident, during an unusual expedition I made to that city of my birth, in the early 1970s. I had just got my degree from UCL and was called up for the military service.

Those days, in Turkey military service was serious business. All young men, the moment they became twenty, were called up to honour their 'patriotic duty' – a cool twenty-six months.

Of course, one quick look at the map would reveal why the Turks attached such importance to military service. The country was surrounded by potential enemies. By north there was the Soviet Union; by east the Middle East, a powder keg at best of times; on the west there was Bulgaria, a Stalinist Soviet Satellite; and in the southwest, Greece, the traditional enemy of Turks.

So, when I reached my 20th year it was my turn to report for the patriotic duty – a prospect which filled me with little enthusiasm. Needless to say, I had used every ruse in the book, to delay it as long as possible – on academic grounds. However, the moment I got my degree from UCL, in International Relations, that door too was hermetically closed. I was facing a major crisis.

What do you expect? I was barely twenty-three years of age, nine years of which had been spent in London – mostly partying. So, the prospect of all that coming to a crushing end on military geopolitical considerations filled me with little enthusiasm.

Besides, would the Soviets really attack Turkey? Sure enough, they were armed to the teeth with nuclear and conventional weapons. However, their real enemy was not Turkey, but the capitalist United States. Besides, if Turks were attacked, being a NATO country, they could always count on the Americans to come to their aid – at least in theory. Therefore, I convinced myself, whether I joined the Turkish army or not would hardly make any difference. My father begged to differ.

'It'll make a man out of you!', he would pontificate, chewing into his cigar.

Of course, what he hoped for was, the military would put the lid on my 'partying' in London, and thereafter, I could be wheeled into joining the Turkish Ministry of Foreign Affairs in Ankara – a prospect which I did not care for much either.

It was obvious, in order to save myself from such calamity, I had to take matters into my own hands; and that is how I ended up, in a particularly freezing January, in Istanbul.

Those days, in the early 1970s, the roadmap for wiggling out of the military was to get oneself declared 'infirm' with a medical certificate, issued by a Military doctor. Naturally, along the way, one had to grease certain palms. Still, does the cookie not crumble that way with most things in life?

Through the grapevine I had heard of a military psychiatrist, a

Colonel Haki, practising at the Istanbul Naval Hospital. The question was how to get to him? I decided to take the bull by the horns. So, one Monday morning I simply turned up at the hospital, situated on the shores of Golden Horn.

I asked at the enquiries desk for Colonel Haki.

'You'll find him in the basement', said the Marine at the reception.

The Department of Psychiatry, in the basement of the Naval Hospital, consisting of an endless corridor, was not for the faint-hearted. On one side there were cells, just like at a prison, separated from the corridor by bars, behind which were inmates – some screaming, some shouting obscenities, some indulging in obscene acts. In their filthy and torn pyjamas, they looked almost 'subhuman' – dishevelled and unkempt. Along the corridor, male orderlies, wearing black capes, paced up and down, supervising. As they moved at a certain pace, their capes billowed, giving them a satanic appearance. The Psychiatric Department of the Istanbul Naval Hospital looked as if, once in, few people ever got out.

Colonel Haki was a man in his mid-forties and, in his navy blue uniform, he looked quite imperious. His face revealed little. He asked me the reason for my visit. Naturally, I could not say: 'I don't feel like doing my military service; so, I am willing to bribe you to get me out of it.' I had to broach the subject tactfully.

So I explained, I had been living in London for nine years and my doctor felt, psychologically, I was unfit for military service. However, I realised, the opinion of a foreign doctor would not count in Turkey, especially for the military, and that is why, I concluded, I needed a Turkish military doctor to support his report. However, when it came to the punch line, as in dropping the necessary hints for 'remuneration', I totally froze.

Colonel Haki looked me up and down in silence. Then he asked a number of questions in rapid succession. He knew his stuff.

'There's nothing wrong with you', he concluded.

That was that... Suddenly I lost my bottle. I realised, if I pushed my luck, I could be arrested on the spot for trying to bribe an officer of the Turkish Navy. I replied,

'Thank you for your time, Sir.'

I got up and swiftly made for the door. Then something very odd happened. As I was just about to let myself out, Colonel Haki said,

'So, you live in England?'

'Yes, Sir.'

There was a pregnant pause. Then I left the room.

I had my chance, and I blew it. As I walked along the Golden Horn, on that freezing January day, I thought I'd better get used to the idea of spending the next twenty-six months with the Turkish Military. Still, something kept ringing in my ears.

'So, you live in London...'

There was an encrypted message in this. But, what was it? The answer hit me as I walked past a public telephone box. Colonel Haki was a shrink and he lived in Istanbul. What if he had a private practice? There was only one way of finding it out.

I dashed into the phone box, picked up the Istanbul telephone directory, and went straight for the letter 'H'. Sure enough, there it was—

'Dr Haki, A.D. Consultant Psychiatrist.'

I noticed, in the phone book, there was no mention of his military rank. However, there was an address, in the upmarket part of Istanbul, and a telephone number.

'Dr Haki's surgery', answered a woman's voice on the telephone. My heart pounding, I mumbled a few words.

'Is it for an appointment?'

'Yes.'

Without further ado, one was given for that afternoon at five.

When I put the phone down, I could not believe how easily I had fixed it – and all on my own.

I turned up on the dot. The address was easy to find, given it was on a Main Street, in the posh part of Istanbul. Dr Haki's surgery was on the third floor of a modern block. A woman in her forties opened the door. I introduced myself.

'Dr Haki is running late, I hope you don't mind waiting.'

'Not at all.'

I was ushered into a waiting room, with thick carpets. There was another patient, a young woman, sitting at an armchair, browsing through a glossy women's magazine. Seeing me settle down, she lifted her eyes and smiled. That was the first time I saw Leyla.

She was in her early twenties, attractive in a 'gamine' way, with long dark hair, an expressive face with big brown eyes. She was slim, with narrow shoulders and long, if slightly muscular legs. She was dressed simply – just a black skirt and a crème coloured blouse which badly hid her tiny but enticing breasts, shadowed by a waistcoat. She had tied a red and yellow silk scarf around her neck, probably, to add a touch of colour. She was wearing wine coloured flats.

Although she looked as if immersed in the glossy women's magazine, I could see out of the corner of my eye that she was studying me. After all, we were not at a doctor's surgery, but in fact at a psychiatrist's, and that fact alone meant we already knew something of each other – that we had 'secrets'.

'I think, it's going to be a long wait' she said finally, trying to make it sound as casual. I did not how to react, given, at that moment in time, all I had in my mind was how to bribe Colonel Haki. So, I mumbled,

'Probably.'

'I haven't seen you here before.'

'I'm new.'

I was hoping my monosyllabic answers would discourage any further attempts to socialise. For a while, we sat in silence. As I buried my head into the five-day old newspaper, she crossed her legs with a quick move, managing to exhibit more of them. Then, with a swift move, pushing her dark hair back, she asked:

'What do you do?'

She certainly did not beat around the bush. I replied,

'I live in London, and—'

Mercifully, I was saved by the bell:

'Dr Haki will see you now' called out the receptionist.

And yet, the young girl was ahead of me. I gave her an apologetic look. She smiled,

'I take ages, that's why he sees me last.' Then, as I got up, she quickly added,

'There's a coffee shop, right across the road, will you wait there for me?'

I was so taken aback by this directness, without thinking, I replied,

'Sure.'

'By the way, my name is Leyla', I heard her say, as I left the waiting room.

Colonel Haki, now out of uniform, in a three piece grey suit, did not look surprised to see me.

'I spent three months in England, in Portsmouth, with the Royal Navy.' he said, picking up the conversation exactly where we had left. Then he quickly came to the point.

'So, you're unfit for the military service?'

96

I suddenly realised there was no point in insulting this man's intelligence with some imaginary ailment. So, I came clean:

'I have been living in England since I was thirteen. I went to school there and then to university. Now I am working as an assistant stage director at the Royal Opera House, with an offer of permanent employment. If I spend twenty-six months in the Military, there will be nothing left of me.'

Colonel Haki listened in silence. Finally, he said,

'I have another patient waiting. Come and see me in one week.'

This time I had played my cards right, and things seemed to be moving in the right direction. As I was leaving, Leyla was ushered in.

* * *

I found the coffee, shop opposite Colonel Haki's surgery, with no trouble. It had a big sign on the window: 'Bosphorus Café.'

As I sat there waiting for Leyla, I reviewed my situation. The truth was, I still had not mentioned a word to Colonel Haki about 'remuneration'. Offering a bribe was an art form, and I had no experience in it. Suddenly, another dark cloud descended on me.

What if I was reading the signs wrong. What if Colonel Haki needed a week, purely to set up a trap for me? What if, next week when I returned, I got arrested, not merely for draft-dodging, but also for attempting to bribe an officer of the Turkish Navy. With so many 'what ifs', I had not noticed the time pass.

'Hope I didn't keep you waiting.'

I looked up, there was Leyla. As she was sitting down, she quickly added,

'I can't stay long, I'm expected home for dinner.'

For a brief moment, I wondered if she was married. She looked in her early twenties, but one never knows. On top of the high-wire act I was trying to perform, the last thing I needed was an affair with a married woman. Turkish husbands, as a rule, did not take kindly to their wives dating other men.

As it turned out, Leyla was not married; she merely lived at home, with her parents. She was an unpretentious young woman, no airs or graces, quite attractive, if slightly tomboyish. She was a student at the Faculty of Fine Arts.

'I'd like to see you again', she said, as she was getting ready to leave.

'I am not going to be in Istanbul for long', I replied, explaining I lived in London.

'What are you doing tomorrow?'

'Nothing much', I answered, again surprised at her directness.

'Let's meet at two. I have to be home for supper.'

Given I had left Istanbul in my early teens, I had no experience of dating in that city. So when asked where to meet, I said the first thing that came to my head.

'How about the Hilton?'

The next day, I sat myself at a quiet corner at The Manhattan Bar at the Istanbul Hilton, nicely tucked away in that vast hotel. Leyla arrived on the dot. This time she was in high heels, black stockings, a mini skirt and a tight black top which emphasised her small but ripe breasts. She had no make-up, except for some eyeshadow, making her huge brown eyes all the more expressive.

'What would you like to have?', I asked.

'Calvados', she replied, trying to sound sophisticated.

Thanks to copious Turkish measures the conversation flowed easily. Leyla was an only child. She had just turned twenty-two and was studying Art History.

'Gets me out of the house', she added.

I had a feeling, on the home front, things were not quite right. Then, came another direct hit.

'Why do you see a psychiatrist?'

'Personal problems…' I replied, thinking on my feet.

'Personal problems?'

'Yes, you know…'

'You can tell me everything.'

'I'd rather not talk about it.'

'You're shy…'

Although I knew my answer did not convince her, mercifully, she decided not to dig any deeper. Instead she asked about my life in London. I explained I had just secured a position at the Royal Opera House, as a trainee stage director.

'You are artistic!', she remarked, delighted.

By then, we had been talking well over an hour, fuelled by generous measures of Calvados. Looking into my eyes, she asked,

'Why did you choose to meet at the Hilton?'

'I couldn't think of anywhere else'. Then, she dropped another bombshell.

'Do you want to go upstairs?'

* * *

Making love with Leyla was sheer delight. It was as if she had been crossing a desert and suddenly found an oasis. Now, she was quenching her thirst. Every little movement, every little touch opened for her a new window. With each touch or a slight movement there was a sigh, a small tremor which, I could feel, reverberated through her young body.

By the time we came to our senses, it had already got dark – It was early January.

'Oh my God, is that the time. My father will kill me!'

With that she jumped out of the bed, quickly got dressed and, just before leaving, gave me a kiss, whispering into my ear:

'Tomorrow, same time.'

From then on, our afternoons were spent with more Calvados sessions. Thanks to my newly acquired American Express card, I kept the room at the Hilton permanently. As for Calvados, thanks to a liquor store I discovered in the Grand Bazaar, run by an Armenian, I stocked up, avoiding room service rates at the Istanbul Hilton.

As days passed, Leyla became more uninhibited, and our Calvados sessions reached new dimensions. Now, she was letting go and, in the process, revealing multiple facets of herself.

One day she turned up with a surprise – a new hairstyle. She had it cut real short, turning herself into a 'Garçon Manquée'. When I remarked on it, at first embarrassed, she said,

'I thought you might like it.'

That day, our Calvados session was more passionate and voluptuous than ever. Leyla had pulled out all the stops and was happy. As we had totally forgotten about time, when we came down to earth, horrified, she said now she had to invent a story in order to appease her father. Adding,

'He's already livid about my short hair.'

It was at that moment, for the first time, I enquired about her father. I was in for another shock.

'He is a General.'

'A general!'

'Yes, commander of the Third Army.'

She went on to explain, that was how she had ended up as a patient of Colonel Haki, the navy psychiatrist.

'He's my father's best friend.'

With that, she was out of the door. As I started dressing I thought, a colonel on one side, a general on the other, what a fine mess had I got myself into. One thing was certain, I was playing with fire.

Days passed quicker than I would have liked. All that time, as our Calvados sessions continued, Leyla was supposed to be attending her lectures at the Faculty of Fine Arts. We even managed to spend an entire weekend together, as Leyla told the General she was staying with a girlfriend who had agreed to model for her.

However, the sands were running out, and soon it was time for me to attend the second appointment with Colonel Haki. So, one Thursday afternoon, with a heavy heart, I turned up at his smart consulting rooms.

The problem was, I still had not worked out how to bribe him without it backfiring. Notwithstanding, I had done some research and found out the going rate for this sort of thing, namely a fake medical certificate, was around US $5,000 – those days not an inconsiderable sum. Now, borrowed from a wealthy friend, that sum was sitting in my pocket, in a brown envelope, in crisp $100 bills.

'Dr Haki will see you now', announced the receptionist.

This was the moment of truth. Either I would wiggle out of the military, or end up in a Turkish prison for attempting to bribe an officer of the Turkish Navy. I just had to take the plunge, and hope for the best.

Colonel Haki greeted me in his usual affable manner.

'Please take a seat.'

However, at that point his phone rung and, apologising, he took the call.

By then, absolutely paranoid, I was sure this was a pre-arranged signal for the military police to storm in and arrest me. Worse still, I had the incriminating evidence sitting neatly in my pocket. The brown envelope containing the $5,000 cash was enough to send me away for quite a long stretch.

However, as far as I could make out, the phone call was about an automobile, a 1970 Chevrolet convertible, that Colonel Haki was interested in buying. The gist of the conversation was his offer has been turned down.

'I'm afraid I can't go any higher', he concluded, as he put the phone down.

Surely, this was the moment to come to his rescue with my $5,000. I slowly reached for the brown envelope in my pocket. However, simultaneously, Colonel Haki too reached for something in his pocket – as if about to pull out a gun.

At that point, a voice in me told me to hold my horses. The last thing I wanted was to be caught red handed, handing over to him a bribe.

However, Colonel Haki did not pull a gun. Instead, what came out of his pocket was an envelope which he handed over to me. Noticing the puzzled look on my face, he said,

'Have a look.'

As I opened the envelope, I recognised the headed stationary of the Naval Hospital. The document was a Medical Certificate, pronouncing me 'psychologically unfit' to serve in the Military. It was signed by Colonel A.D. Haki, Senior Consultant Psychiatrist, Naval Hospital, Istanbul. It was also adorned by countless official stamps under his signature.

'I still owe you…', said Colonel Haki.

It was at that point I realised there was something more to it all than met the eye. Colonel Haki continued,

'In one single week you've achieved what I failed to do, over three years.'

'I beg your pardon?'

'Leyla… She finally did it.'

'I'm not sure I follow you, Sir.'

'She told me everything.'

'What exactly?'

'The Calvados sessions.'

Only then I realised, everything meant *everything*.

It would appear, while we were having our Calvados sessions, Leyla still had found time to keep her twice weekly appointments with Colonel Haki. By the time he finished explaining, I realised she had left nothing to imagination.

'From now on she will lead a normal, healthy life. You've broken the spell.'

Still in shock, I mumbled something, vaguely referring to the $5,000 sitting in my pocket. Colonel Haki sensed where I was coming from.

'This one is on me'. Then, speechless, as I was taking my leave, he added,

'Send me a postcard from Piccadilly Circus.'

By the time I left Colonel Haki's rooms it had already got dark – After it was still January.

As I walked along the posh Istanbul street, looking at shop windows, I noticed, it was snowing in big flakes. I decided to leave for London as soon as possible.

What do you know, Leyla came to the airport to see me off. She had brought a parting present – a bottle of vintage Calvados. She was strong, full of fun, and did not make the slightest emotional scene. As I was about to go through the immigration, she told me she had decided to leave her parents' house and move in with a girlfriend – the one she used for her alibi during our Calvados sessions.

Sadly, although I had given her my address in London, I never heard from her again. She had too much dignity for that.

Looking back on it, I suppose, I had served my purpose in her life, as she in mine. It was one of those moments, when everything perfectly fell into place, so what would be the point in spoiling it?

ALLEGRO CON BRIO

The Nag's Head, an old-fashioned English pub, is situated directly opposite the stage door of the Royal Opera House, on Floral Street in Covent Garden. As such, it is the usual watering hole of the members of the orchestra who, in common with their colleagues world over, have never been adverse to the odd tipple or two. Indeed, I often used to wonder why the orchestra sounded much more lively in the second and third acts, until I realised it was simply due to the aforementioned. fact – namely, during the intervals the players sneaked out to the pub, literally, to have a quick one. In fact, the management of the Royal Opera had arranged for a bell to be installed at the Nag's Head, to ring simultaneously with the house bells, reminding the audience, and the wayward players, the performance was about to start. So, the orchestra players would gulp their pints and swiftly step across the road, disappearing through the Stage Door, to take their seats in the orchestra pit. Naturally, once the performance was over, they would return to the 'The Nag's', to have 'one for the road'.

That is how I met Atilla, after a performance of 'Don Pasquale'.

Leaning against the bar, I was having a pint of Guinness, when someone tapped me on the shoulder,

'Could you keep an eye on this, I need to spend a penny.'

With that he handed me a violin case and disappeared, to deal with the call of nature. He was a man in his early thirties, with a goatee beard, and seemed quite affable.

I used to love 'Nags' for its artistic atmosphere. Indeed, if you were a tourist, you might wonder why most of the patrons were always in black tie and tails. Although, the various musical instruments scattered around the place, in their black cases, might have given the game away. In those days, in early 1970s, I was working as an assistant stage director, 'teaboy', at the Royal Opera. I too used to spend a fair bit of time at Nag's Head.

'Can I buy you a drink?'

It was the owner of the instrument, who had just returned from satisfying a call of nature. Having accepted the offer, as we were clinking glasses, I told him,

'You are a trusting man. I could've walked with your violin.'

'I've seen you around.'

He spoke with a thick accent. This was not unusual, given some of the orchestral players in London were Eastern Europeans.

'You're not English, are you?' I asked.

'I'm Turkish.'

That was the beginning of our friendship. Naturally, when I revealed to him I too was Turkish, we hit it off instantly.

Atilla was the head of the viola section in the orchestra. Perhaps I should explain, being a head of a section in an orchestra is quite a responsible job, as that person leads all the instruments in that particular section – be it violins, violas, celli, woodwinds etc.

Moreover, given the Royal Opera House Orchestra often played under the baton of legendary conductors – Karl Böhm, Wolfgang Sawallisch, Georg Solti, Otto Klemperer to name a few, as a section head you would be responsible to make sure your team followed the conductor's directions with precision.

Over a few pints, Atilla told me, first he had studied the violin at the Ankara conservatory then, on a state scholarship, he was sent to London, to the Royal College of Music.

'If you studied the violin, how come you now play the viola?' I asked.

'It's a long story…'

He spoke Turkish also with a dialect, which betrayed he was not from Istanbul and, probably, from a humble background. Evidently, his undisputed talent more than compensated for that. Given, by then, we were having our third round, I allowed myself to ask,

'Apart from the Walton Viola Concerto, what else is there in the Viola repertoire?'

'Not much.'

'So, why change from Violin to viola?'

Here is what had happened. At RCM Atilla had a girlfriend, a violin student – 'a blond with huge green eyes'. One day they had a tiff and, in the heat of the argument, the blond snapped:

'And do you call yourself a violinist!'

That did it. Atilla picked up his violin, and hitting it against his leg, he smashed it into pieces.

'Here is your violin!' he riposted.

'Ever since that day, I've never touched the instrument.'

I wanted to cry out, 'Bloody idiot!', but had the common sense to bite my tongue. Instead, I asked,

'And what happened to the girl?'

'I married her.'

Pleased to have found someone willing to listen to him – at that a compatriot, as we were parting, he said,

'Come to dinner, this Sunday?'

* * *

Like most musicians, Atilla lived in North London – in Highgate, at a block of flats. As prescribed, 7 pm on the dot, armed with a bottle of Gevrey Chambertin 1962, I rung the doorbell.

I was in for a thunderbolt: The door was opened by this divine creature who, without the shadow of a doubt, was the most sensuous woman I had ever set my eyes upon.

'I'm Rachel' she said, with an inviting smile, 'come on in.'

She had huge green eyes, and her long blond mane ran all the way down to her waist. In her early thirties, she was tall and slender. Her shapely legs went on forever. She was wearing a black skirt, low heeled shoes, a simple black top. She had small breasts, but managed to accentuate them, with the help of an uplift bra – indeed, behind her tight black top, I could detect her pert nipples. Apart from a touch of eyeshadow, she had no make-up; nor was she wearing any earrings. With a slight Northern accent, in a husky voice, she spoke in quick short sentences. I do not mind admitting, I was instantly attracted to her.

Their flat was small, but tastefully furnished, with a large Chesterfield sofa with lots of cushions on it. The walls were covered with photographs of Atilla – performing chamber music with various musicians – Georg Solti, Daniel Barenboim, Yehudi Menuhin, Idil Biret…

During dinner, as the wine flowed, so did the conversation. I got to know some bits about Rachel. Although a violinist, her life had not panned out the way Atilla's had. After graduating from RCM, the Royal College of Music, she never played professionally – even at a remote desk in an orchestra. Instead, having married Atilla, and born him two daughters, she ended up as a mother and a wife. As for music, she contented herself to teaching at a primary school in Belsize Park, and occasionally giving private lessons. Against that backdrop, Atilla was the undisputed star.

Our evening was spent with chatting about life, and how it was full of surprises. A case in point being my own experience. How, years ago, having arrived in England to attend summer school, in order to learn English, I ended up living in London.

'What I really wanted was to go to New York…' I added.

'I once played at the Carnegie Hall, when I was with the LSO.' Attila responded.

'Beethoven 5, LSO nil…' Rachel butted in.

Atilla gave her a sharp look, pretending to laugh… Then noticing my puzzled look, he went on to explain.

'We were to play Beethoven's Fifth. In the first movement, Allegro Con Brio, you can either do a 'reprise' or carry on. For some reason, at the rehearsals, this point was not clarified. So, during the performance, when we came to the famous Ostinato, 'Fate knocking at the door', half the orchestra carried on, while the other half went back to the beginning. A real fuck up.' Atilla concluded.

'Beethoven 5, LSO nil…' Rachel added, 'That's what Harold Schonberg wrote in the New York Times, the next day.'

'Schonberg never wrote that!' retorted Atilla.

'Yes he did' insisted Rachel, 'And I read it!'

'Check your facts!'

'Stop giving me lessons!'

'You need one!' retorted Atilla, asserting himself. Rachel sprung to her feet,

'I'll leave you guys to it…' and marched out of the room.

'Fuck her…' Atilla said.

Given, by then, it was well past midnight. Looking at my watch, I exclaimed,

'My God, is that the time!'

And, with that, having thanked Atilla for a great evening, I took my leave.

As I was driving through the deserted roads of North London, I was reflecting about the scene I had just witnessed. I felt like punching Atilla on the nose. That was when I realised I had fallen in love with his wife.

* * *

From that day on I became a regular visitor to their home. Atilla was only too happy to have found another Turk to talk to. Of course, given ROH Orchestra played both for the opera and the ballet companies, it meant Atilla worked almost every night. Consequently, the only evening I could pay a visit to Highgate was Sundays. And, sure enough, each Sunday, armed with a bottle of Chateau Margot or Gevrey Chambertin, I turned up at Highgate.

Be that as it may, there was no question whatsoever of acting upon my feelings for Rachel. Under normal circumstances, the fact that she was a married woman would hardly have stopped me from trying my luck – come what may. Only, for some reason, because her husband was Turkish, I just could not bring myself to even think about having my feelings known to Rachel.

As for her, although people say 'women sense these things', I do not think she had any feelings towards me beyond the fact that I had become a pal to her husband.

Given Atilla and I worked in the same building, on the nights I was on duty – to look after a revival of an old production – and he was playing in the pit, after the performance, we inevitably ended up at the Nag's for a quick one, then set out in search of a place to have dinner. This often meant Camden Town – those days a bohemian part of London where out of work actors, pop musicians and artists of all descriptions had congregated.

Once out of the Camden Town tube station, we would do the rounds of various kebab joints, while Atilla, standing outside each establishment, scrutinised the menus – a habit which used to drive me crazy. Then, once he gave the green light, we could finally settle down to have our dinner.

Naturally, in those kebab joints, a man entering in white tie and tails, with a violin case, attracted a certain amount of attention. On one of those occasions, the owner of the establishment, speaking with a thick Cypriot accent, asked Atilla,

'You play violin, no?'

Not to complicate matters – as in explaining the instrument in question was actually a viola, Atilla answered curtly.

'Yes.' The Cypriot pushed on,

'Come play here. I pay you £10 a night, cash in hand, and you get free dinner.'

I felt I had to come to his rescue. I explained, Atilla played with the Royal Opera House Orchestra. As I was about to add he was, in fact, the principal viola, the Cypriot cut me off,

'Extra cash doesn't hurt.'

In time I got to know Atilla a little better – although, he was not an easy man to know or, perhaps, there was not much to know about him. His life seemed to consist of music and, as is the case with most musicians, of sex. Given, he had a well-built physique and beard, he exuded megawatt masculine energy, and women were instantly attracted to him.

As for me, in the ROH orchestra, there was a certain woman, a young Argentinian cellist, whom I adored. In Eugene Onegin by Tchaikovsky, the doomed hero of the piece, Lensky, just before being killed in a duel, sings an arioso, philosophising about the meaning of life. That piece had a long solo introduction played on the cello; and, although I did not care much for Tchaikovsky, I used to go to every performance of Onegin – purely in order to watch my Argentinian Amazon. The fact that the technical requirements of playing the said instrument – as in, placing it between one's legs, while they inevitably had to be kept wide open, made Tchaikovsky's music more palatable. Luckily, the staff box at ROH was logistically positioned, right above the orchestra pit.

One night, after another performance of Onegin, as we were having our pints at the Nag's, I confessed to Atilla my fantasies about the Argentinian.

'I fucked her silly, under the railway bridge, right against the wall, by the Festival Hall, when we were with the LSO' revealed Atilla.

'I bet you had every female player in the Royal Opera Orchestra.' I commented.

'And the BBC Symphony, LSO, plus the Royal Philharmonic…'

* * *

As months passed, in view of the countless dinners I had invited myself to Atilla's home, purely to admire his wife, I thought it was high time that it should be reciprocated.

'Let's go and have a nice meal, on your night off!' I suggested.

Atilla was having none of it.

'I will not let you spend money you don't have in expensive restaurants' he protested. 'Either we come to yours, or we're not coming at all.'

Finally, on the prescribed day, at 7 pm punctually, armed with a bottle of Sainsbury's wine, Atilla rung my doorbell. Rachel, was in a sexy red number generously exhibiting her pert breasts and her long shapely legs. As usual, she was wearing some sexy low heeled shoes with a hole in the front, exhibiting her toenails painted in red. Her blond hair was done up in a chignon, and she wore huge hoops as earrings. To top it all off, she was wearing a most sensuous perfume which immediately filled my huge sitting room. That was the first time I had an inkling, after all, she might not have been totally blind to my feelings for her. As luck would have it, to stop me from ogling her all night, I had also invited an ex-girlfriend, Maureen – a 'bunny' at the Playboy club.

Dinner, which I had the common sense to order from a Chinese Restaurant, went without a hitch. As wine flowed, so did the conversation. Atilla was absolutely fascinated by Maureen who candidly confessed she had never been to a 'classical music' concert, adding,

'In Birmingham, we hardly had anything like that…'

'I'm playing in Birmingham next week – with Georg Solti's Quartet' said Atilla.

'What's a String Quartet?'

'It shouldn't really be called a Quartet—' butted in Rachel.

'And why not, Ms Know-it-all?', retorted Atilla.

'Cause, it's only three strings – violin, viola, cello, plus a piano.'

'Piano has strings…'

'It's a percussion instrument!'

At that point, I noticed Maureen rolling something in her hand.

'Wanna have a joint?' she asked Rachel.

'Great! Now you're a junkie…' yelped Atilla.

'I just want to see what it tastes like…'

Mercifully, soon, thanking me for the great evening they got up to leave. However, as they were leaving, suddenly, with a smile, Atilla turned to Maureen,

'I'll leave a ticket for you at the box office. It's next Saturday, 17th…'

* * *

During the following weeks, I did not see much of Atilla, as I was immersed in rehearsals of Don Giovanni – a new production with technical problems. In the final scene, when Don Giovanni is supposed to be taken to hell for his misdeeds by the stone statue, the trap door kept getting stuck. Consequently, by the end of the opera, the baritone playing the part was still on stage, wondering what to do with himself. The problem was finally fixed; and after the dress rehearsal, as I was having a pint at the Nag's, I had the proverbial tap on my shoulder.

'Care for a pint?'

Atilla seemed to be more chuffed with himself than usual. Soon I discovered why. Maureen had come to his recital in Birmingham.

'She wanted to hear a string quartet.' Atilla mitigated.

'What we're you playing?' I asked.

'Schubert, Death and the Maiden. She loved it.'

* * *

After that, for some reason, Atilla and I didn't see much of each other. I also stopped inviting myself to dinners at Highgate. By then, I probably had purged Rachel out of my system. Be that as it may, a few months later, when I ran into Atilla at the Nag's, I just could not help asking after her.

'She's now at the Adelphi, playing for My Fair Lady.'

Directed by the writer himself – Alan Jay Lerner, the show was huge hit, running well over 300 performances.

'That's great news!' I exclaimed.

'It's the first time ever she's ever played in an orchestra' commented Atilla, adding, 'It's only a musical.'

A few weeks later, something odd took place. After a performance of La Sonnambula, as I was waiting for a number 11 bus on the Strand, my eyes caught a young couple, leaning against the bus stop, snogging in throes of passion. Then, the girl suddenly turned around her head, and I came face to face with Rachel. She was with a delicate looking man, in his early twenties. For a few seconds, in disbelief, we kept looking into each other's eyes. Then, she broke into hysterical laughter.

I smiled back, as if to say her secret was safe with me. Naturally, the young fellow did not have a clue about what was going on. Finally, Rachel put her arms around him, with her long blond mane drowning his face, and continued devouring him. Mercifully, a few minutes later a number 11 bus showed up, and I swiftly hopped on it.

Some weeks later, at the Nag's, I had the proverbial tap on my shoulder.

'Care for a pint?'

This time, however, Atilla was not his usual brash self. In fact, he looked decidedly in a sombre mood. As we were sipping our pints, he announced,

'I'm divorcing Rachel.'

'Oh?'

'The bitch has been screwing around!'

'Are you sure?' I asked, feigning surprise.

'She confessed everything.'

'She did?'

'She's been having it off with the piccolo player.'

'I can't believe it.'

'So much for My Fair *fucking* Lady!'

Knowing Atilla's temperament, I saw little sense in pointing out for years he had been committing the same misdemeanour – of which he now was accusing his wife. Oddly, as if he had read my thoughts, he added,

'It's not the same for a man.'

Some months later, I heard through the grapevine that Atilla and Rachel were divorced. Moreover, he left a huge house which he just had bought, to her. When I met him next, he was living in a bedsit in Belsize Park.

'I walked out with the clothes I was standing in…' he announced, with glee.

* * *

God works in mysterious ways. Soon enough, Atilla met another woman – a Jewish lady from South Africa. She was considerably older than him, slightly plump, and not exactly an oil painting – especially after Rachel. However, soon they were married, and moved into a large house on Hampstead Heath. In fact, true to what they say, she turned out to be a real Jewish Mama – doting on Atilla as if he was a God. She would go around saying her husband was 'world famous virtuoso in Turkey'.

By then, having moved into film business, I no longer saw Atilla. However, one day we ran into each other at the Nag's Head, again after a performance of Don Giovanni – which I had attended as a paying member of the audience. For old times' sake, as we were sipping our pints, I asked in jest,

'Do you still play the field?'

'God forbid' He answered. 'Why chase hamburgers when you have steak at home?'

As I left the pub, the Floral Street was full of after première crowd of Don Giovanni – men in black tie, with their elegant ladies in long dresses – I could not help thinking of a saying by Molière, 'La grande ambition des femmes est d'inspirer de l'amour.'

CANCER

Erol slowly inserted the key into the lock, then discretely pushed the door open to his flat. It was about 6 am, a warm August morning. He had spent the night in the arms of a sensuous 21-year-old brunette, Kathy, an Australian piano student at the Royal College of Music, ten years his junior. Still, at thirty-one, Erol felt in peak condition.

Musicians are such a randy lot, he thought as he tiptoed into his flat, adding, so what... You only live once. He was being extra careful not to make any noise, as his mother, who lived in Geneva, was staying with him, on a brief visit.

Although Turkish, when he retired, Erol's father bought a small house on the shores of Lake Geneva, which had been his lifetime dream, and that is how his parents ended up in Switzerland. However, within a year, his father died with a heart attack, and ever since, his mother's visits to London became more and more frequent. As Erol slowly opened the door into his bedroom, a voice from the sitting room said:

'And where do you think you are going!'

When Erol looked in, he could see his mother standing in the middle of the sitting room, her arms crossed, in her silk negligée and high-heeled slippers.

'Do you know what the time is!'

Looking at his watch, Erol replied:

'Five minutes after six. What seems to be the problem?'

'You have to ask?'

'Well, yes.'

'Couldn't you have called?'

Trying to keep his composure, Erol answered,

'Mother, I just went out to dinner. Then, we were listening to music, chatting, and…'

'Chatting! Didn't she have a phone, your hooker?'

'She is not a hooker!'

'She spends the night with a total stranger, and she's not a hooker?'

'I am not a total stranger, and she is a second-year piano student at the Royal College of Music.'

'So what?'

'So… she's not a—'

'I was about to call the police!'

'Police?'

On that note, she threw herself onto the sofa, gasping for breath, as if choking:

'I thought something had happened to you…'

If slightly over the top, it was all the same an impressive performance. Indeed, had she chosen to go into the acting profession, she could easily have been a great tragedian – a Sarah Bernhardt, Bette Davis or Gloria Swanson. Moreover, Erol knew from past experience, once in this mood, his mother could go on forever. In fact, since her husband had died, she found her feet and blossomed into an unbridled woman.

'I'm sorry, I should've called.' Erol said, in order to curtail the performance.

She gave him a sharp look, as if the carpet had been pulled from underneath her feet. However, he gave her a hug, and with that, he was now able to send her off to her bedroom – which was his own, now on loan to his mother. As she was retiring, she sighed as if choking.

'You just don't understand…'

'What?'

'What it means to be a mother.'

With that, her performance cut short, she shut the door behind her.

Suddenly, Erol felt tired. While, when he arrived, he was on top of the world – confident, happy and full of zest; now he felt beat, miserable and soiled. He quickly threw a blanket and a pillow on the sofa, lied down and closed his eyes…

Erol reflected. He was thirty-one and still unmarried. Yet London, where he lived since the age of thirteen, was full of attractive and intelligent women, but how could he possibly introduce a prospective wife to his mother? More to the point, which young woman could take her on, as a mother-in-law!

With these thoughts, and the previous night's activities now catching up with him, Erol finally fell asleep.

Months went by and, with his mother now back in Switzerland, Erol's life was back to normal. In fact, he was almost feeling guilty for having sent her packing to Geneva, within days of the last episode. Still, thanks to that, Erol had regained his freedom, more to the point, his sanity. Now, he was once more able to enjoy his bachelor life, playing the field to his heart's content.

Indeed, he was now seeing a beautiful 23-year-old blond, Isabelle whom he met at a friend's birthday party. Isabelle was half Scottish half English, with some Swedish ancestry thrown in for good measure. She had huge cobalt blue eyes, and her blond hair ran down to her waist. Her skin had a translucent quality, which accentuated the features of her face. She had long, most shapely legs, which went on forever. She spoke with a touch of a Scottish accent which, coupled with her naturally husky voice, made her all the more sensuous. In short, Izzy, as she called herself, was fun.

She had no airs or graces. Her father was an actor, and mother a music teacher. Educated at one of the elitist schools in England, Bedales, she had not bothered with university. Instead, she chose to work as a barmaid at the Savoy, on Strand – where, over the years, all the Greats of the British theatre, Noel Coward, Sybil Thorndike, Peter Ustinov, Laurence Olivier used to drink. In fact, if working at the Savoy Bar had not been a part of Izzy's catering course, Erol would have never met her.

She valued her independence immensely, and attached great importance to Work Ethic. Indeed, apart from her sensuous looks, she was very much 'her own man'. She was not the type of woman one could impress with expensive gifts, or by being taken to five-star restaurants…

In the beginning, Erol thought his fascination for Izzy was a fleeting romance – a combination of physical attraction and infatuation.

As months passed, he realised, she was like no other woman he had ever met before: Izzy had something Erol could not quite put his finger on.

In her presence, he felt elated, as if defying gravity. Other notions of physics didn't seem to apply either. Time, for example, seemed to have become quite blurred. When in her company, he did not know where the hours went. When Erol looked into Izzy's cobalt blue eyes, behind them, he could see an ocean. In short, he was in love.

'So, that's what it's like', he thought to himself. This is what all the poets, writers, philosophers, musicians described, but failed to define.

Still, Erol realised, 'being in love' had nothing to do with 'loving someone'; nor was it desiring someone for sex. Also, being in love was pleasurable and painful at the same time.

Suddenly, Erol's life acquired meaning. It was as if until then he did not exist, or had been asleep and, suddenly, with a potion, he was woken up. This was magic. Naturally, he had no idea where all this was going to lead; but, for now, he wanted to live for the day.

Of course, there was a reason for it – the fear of losing her. How could he possibly introduce Izzy to his mother? No young woman, to date, had survived meeting her. Mother had seen to that.

She had a wide range of weapons at her disposal, which, ever since Erol started dating, she had put to most effective use. Her favourite trick was, once in the presence of 'the enemy', i.e. a girlfriend, to take out a small value bank note from her handbag, and slip it into Erol's hand, adding with a smile,

'Darling, just in case…'

Trick number two, equally lethal, involved treating the 'predator' to Erol's childhood photographs. To this end, she had compiled a special photo album which she would exhibit with running commentary.

'His first day at school… Poor darling, he was so terrified he peed in his pants.'

If all failed, then, it was necessary to bring in the big guns – the Telephone Ploy. This involved, by hook or crook, laying her hands on the girl's phone number, then calling her in the wee hours:

'Is my son with you?'

On one occasion, this had triggered the response it deserved.

'Madam, it is 3 am in the morning! Why should I know, or care, who your son is fucking!'

Still, the phone ploy never failed. Within days Erol would be told by the female in question,

'Maybe it's best we give it a break…'

However, at present Erol was dancing on thin air, and he did not wish to spoil that feeling by thinking of his mother.

Izzy, did not demand much. Occasionally, if the weather was nice, they would meet at a small park, at the back of the Savoy. There, they would sit, have an ice cream or tea, and watch the boats pass by on the Thames, chatting for hours.

As for Erol, he knew she was 'the one'. He was walking on cloud number nine. So much so that, one day, when talking with his mother on the phone, he let the cat out of the bag. Trying to explain why, as expected, he could not fly out to Geneva at a hat's drop, he said,

'I met this girl and... I like her a lot.'

This was the first time Erol had ever opened up to his mother about his personal life. Probably, subconsciously, he was preparing her for the big announcement – yet to come.

Weeks passed and Erol's relationship with Izzy grew closer. Indeed, a friend of his even dropped a hint,

'You ought to make your move, soon.'

Erol had been thinking along the same lines; however, fearful of 'soon' being 'too soon', he had been unable to take the plunge.

'That sort of thing could backfire...', he answered. His friend replied,

'Better backfire, than not fire at all!'

Sill, Erol had a plan. He was going to take Izzy to Annabel's – an exclusive might club in London, where the Establishment, movie stars, billionaires, the Aristocracy – even occasionally Prince Charles, let their hair down. Erol figured, that would signal to Izzy how serious he was about her. He thought, 'let the night take care of... the rest'. Finally, a date was made – the following Thursday.

Then, on the Wednesday before, Erol decided to pop out to Harrods and buy himself a new double-breasted blazer, for the occasion. When he got home, he decided to try it on. Since he now was going to the gym, he had got into shape, looking toned and suave. It was at that point the phone rang. It was his mother, calling from Switzerland.

'Darling, I have bad news', she said, in a melodramatic tone.

Erol knew, when his mother wanted something done on the spot, she always started by announcing some imminent tragedy… However, this time, her voice had a darker undertone, signalling a modicum of fear.

'What seems to be to problem?'

'I have a swollen tonsil…'

Realising this was going to be a long call, Erol sat down.

'I went to see Dr Bourgeois,…'

'And?'

'And he said, Je regret, Madame, mais vous avez le Cancer.'

Trying to sound calm, Erol replied,

'Don't worry, we'll deal with it.'

'Dr Bourgeois has already made an appointment with a consultant in Geneva.'

'I'll fly in tomorrow.'

This certainly put the lid on Annabel's and all the meticulous planning that had gone into it. However, this was a real emergency, and there was no alternative.

The professor of Oncology at Hôpitaux Universitaires de Genève, HUG, confirmed non-Hodgkin lymphoma. In fact, even Erol could see the enormous tonsil on the left side of his mother's throat. However, the Swiss professor did not seem to be fussed.

'I can get rid of it in no time.'

'How?'

'Radiotherapy.'

Then he explained, he could start the radiation therapy in three weeks' time, twice weekly sessions.

'Why wait three weeks?', asked Erol.

'It is not too advanced', explained the Swiss professor, 'Also, I'm about to go on holiday.' After a pause, he asked,

'Do you have medical insurance?'

After the hospital, Erol took his mother to the Hotel des Bergues, overlooking Lake Geneva, for a morale boosting lunch. She loved that restaurant, given it was a favourite haunt of the Turks. During lunch, neither Erol nor his mother mentioned the *C* word. However, as they were having coffee, Erol finally spoke.

'I have been thinking, Mother. The place for… this ailment is the Royal Marsden Hospital, in London.'

Of course, the real reason for this suggestion was, Erol just did not want to be stuck in Geneva for months, while his mother was having radiotherapy. It would certainly mean the end of Izzy.

That night, Erol helped his mother pack, making sure she took enough clothes for a long stay. The next morning, a Friday, they were on the first Swissair flight to London.

* * *

The same afternoon, mother and son were at Harley Street, seeing a consultant, specialising in Cancer. Erol had already arranged everything by calling his own private GP, before leaving Geneva.

The consultant's diagnosis was the same – It was lymphoma all right. However, unlike the Swiss specialist, he advised the tonsil should come out as soon as possible, as it had already grown considerably.

'I'll operate on Monday.'

'But it's already Friday?'

The consultant called the Royal Marsden Hospital and booked the operating theatre, and a room, there and then. He told Erol, he should check her mother in as of Sunday night, given she would be first on his operating list for Monday morning.

As, the mother & son were in the cab, leaving Harley Street, Erol tried to make light of the situation.

'Well, you'll be as good as new in no time!'

124

The operation went without a hitch. However, the real news came after the offending item was removed, and sent for culture. The tumour was indeed malignant. Given one did not know if the cancer had already spread to other parts, to be on the safe side, a course of chemotherapy was indicated. The consultant announced:

'She must stay in London.'

Weeks passed, with Erol's mother living in Erol's flat in London. As usual, he had given up his own bedroom, and returned to sleeping on the sofa in the sitting room.

Their days revolved around the treatment for the cancer. Erol had to take his mother, twice a week, for chemotherapy sessions, to the Royal Marsden Hospital on Fulham Road. By now, he discovered, chemotherapy was a euphemism for pure poison. Indeed, as a result of this, his mother's general health deteriorated drastically. She was nauseous with dizzy spells, and generally feeling weak.

Still, Erol took all this in his stride. After all, being in London, as opposed to having to do the same thing in Geneva, meant he could still see Izzy between chemotherapy sessions, and that was what really mattered.

So, Izzy and Erol resumed their visits to the small park behind the Savoy, chatting for hours, having ice cream, and watching the boats pass by on the Thames. Sometimes they even managed to put in a show – 'Mamma Mia', as Izzy loved ABBA.

That was an enchanted evening. After the show, they went to dinner at a romantic Italian restaurant, Giovanni's, tucked away on a tiny alleyway in Covent Garden. However, suddenly, Erol started hearing voices in his mind: It was his friend talking to him,

'You ought to make your move.'

Also, noticing the questioning looks in Izzy's cobalt blue eyes,

Erol realised not only the time had come, but the opportunity was slowly slipping away. He needed to offer some explanation. So, he took a deep breath and came clean. He explained his predicament: his mother's illness, chemotherapy sessions, and inevitably, for the time being, her staying in his flat in Knightsbridge. Izzy reacted compassionately:

'Poor woman…'

Then, she dropped a bomb:

'I'd like to visit her.'

'No! I mean, not yet…'

Erol quickly composed himself, and started lying through his teeth – due to the treatment his mother had been losing her hair, and really did not want to show herself to anyone, while in that state.

'Female pride…' Erol concluded.

Then quickly changing the subject, he asked her what her favourite ABBA song was.

When they left Giovanni's, given it was a balmy November night, instead of taking a cab, Erol walked Izzy to her flat in Bloomsbury, which she shared with another girl. As they walked across Soho, holding hands, he heard another voice in his mind:

'With a bit of luck, she will not make it to the end of the year…'

In early December some more lumps appeared on his mother's body – under her armpits, stomach and her neck. The consultant examined her thoroughly, taking some samples. A few days later the consultant wanted to see Erol – on his own. He did not beat around the bush.

'I'm afraid Chemotherapy isn't working. I'm going to stop everything.'

'What do mean?'

'Take her back to Switzerland and give her a nice Christmas.'

'What about the lumps?'

'Chemotherapy will only make her life miserable, with no beneficial effects.'

'Then what?' Erol asked.

'Then… Swiss doctors can provide palliative care – morphine and that sort of thing…'

'How long?'

'Hope for the best, and prepare for the worst – probably a few months…'

When Erol left the Hospital, he was totally guilt ridden about the thoughts he had on the night when he was walking Izzy home. How could he possibly wish his own mother dead! He had tempted the Gods, and this was the result!

'You are a monster, no less!', he murmured to himself.

Although it was December, Erol decided to walk to Knightsbridge – as he needed to collect his thoughts. He needed a strategy. How could he announce to his mother, as of now, all treatment was stopping? So, they might as well return to Switzerland and have a nice Christmas. No dupe by any stretch of imagination, Erol's mother was bound to smell a rat. Perhaps, he should take a deep breath and come clean – as in, telling her she only had a few months left to live.

When Erol arrived at his flat, surprisingly, he found his mother in an exceptionally exuberant mood. In fact, this was the first time, since the business started, he had seen her so cheerful.

'Darling where have you been!' she asked, flirtatious.

Then, Erol noticed about a dozen fresh white roses in a vase, on the piano. There were also two teacups staring at him.

'Why didn't you tell me before?' Erol's mother asked.

'Tell you what?'

'What an absolutely charming girl she is, of course!'

At that point, Erol's saw, lying open on the sofa, the proverbial photo album – consisting purely of his childhood photos, starting from when he was in his pram, to his first day at school.

'Who was here?', he asked, as if he did not know the answer.

'Why, Isabelle of course! Look, the lovely flowers she brought.'

'Very nice', muttered Erol.

'I kept her as long as I could, hoping you'd turn up. To pass the time, I showed her your childhood album. She absolutely adored it… Where were you?'

'Nowhere…' answered Erol.

Having cleared the coffee table, his mother went into the kitchen. Erol could hear her singing away:

Quand tu me prends dans tes bras,
Et tu me parles tout bas…

* * *

Christmas in Switzerland was indeed a happy event. Erol had decided not to whisper a word about what the consultant had told him. Instead, as advised, he gave his mother a most cheerful time. He took her to lunches at her favourite haunts – Hotel des Bergues in Geneva, Beau-Rivage Palace in Ouchy, and the Montreux Palace. One sunny December day, the mother and son even drove to Gstaad and lunched at the Palace Hotel.

She was as happy as a lark. So, what was the point of spilling the beans and spoiling everything?

Then, in the New Year, in January, something quite extraordinary happened. Erol noticed all the lumps on his mother's body seem to have disappeared. Still, what did he know about Oncology? So, to be on the safe side, he brought her back to London. At the Royal Marsden, even the consultant seemed to be baffled:

'The cancer seems to have gone into remission. It's inexplicable!'
That was in January 1991.

Erol's mother lived on another nineteen years and finally passed away, at the ripe old age of age of eighty-seven.

By the way, when Erol returned to London with his mother from that fateful Christmas in Geneva, he found a letter waiting for him. As he picked up the envelope, he recognised Izzy's handwriting.

The letter said that over Christmas, she had been thinking about 'things' and maybe it was best that they should take a break from seeing each other. She added, she had enjoyed the time they had spent together, and hoped that Erol meets someone to make him happy, etc.

A TRIP TO VIENNA

In the early 1960s Istanbul only a few people owned a private car, and my father was one of them. He had a Citroën which, some years later, was made famous as the TV detective Maigret's car; but, those days, it was simply referred to as a 'Traction Avant' – French for a front wheel drive.

Sadly, my father could not drive. Consequently, he employed a chauffeur – an affable fellow, in his late twenties, who had come to Istanbul from the provinces, and was happy to have found a position with a well to do employer, for whom he did not have to do a lot. In fact, beyond driving my father, in the morning, to his office – a ten-minute journey and, at the end of the working day, repeating the same journey in the opposite direction, the chauffeur had little else to.

Indeed, it was in his spare time, during my school holidays, he taught me to drive. So, practising in the backstreets of Istanbul, in no time I became quite proficient behind the wheel. So much so that, in turn, over the weekends, I taught my father to drive; and, as soon as he passed his driving test, he sacked the chauffeur – an event, to this day, I feel quite guilty about. But at the time, I was barely fifteen.

Be it as it may, to celebrate, my father sold the old 'Traction Avant' and bought himself a new car. As it happened, that year, Citroën had brought out a new model with a modernist design – the DS.

In fact, this was a play on words, which the French language lends itself quite naturally: DS, spelled as 'Déesse', also means a Goddess. Furthermore, Citroën DS was made instantly famous, as General de Gaulle had adopted it as the official presidential car.

At any rate, on with the celebrations, my father announced that we – himself, my mother and I, were going on a driving trip – to Vienna!

'What's wrong with flying?', was my mother's first reaction.

Although my father was a successful self-made businessman, my mother, his second wife and fourteen years his junior, came from 'old money'. So, not only had she grown up with a squadron of nannies, but she was also surrounded by private cars and chauffeurs. Consequently, as far as she was concerned, purchasing a new automobile hardly constituted a cause for celebration.

Be that as it may, one September morning we set out from Istanbul – destination Vienna. The idea was to make it to Sofia, the capital of Bulgaria, in one go, and spend the night there. My father added,

'In the old days, it was called Le Petit Paris.'

However, after some seven hours of driving, when we arrived, Le Petit Paris had in store for us a small surprise. As my father handed over our passports to the receptionist at the Balkan Palace, the latter denied, point blank, any knowledge of a reservation. By sheer coincidence, they were also fully booked.

Given, my father organised everything in his life with an eye to the minutest detail – with the precision of a general planning a military campaign, this was a red rag to the bull:

'Ce n'est pas possible!' He roared.

Undaunted, the Bulgarian receptionist repeated:

'Pas de réservation.'

However, having just driven 600 kilometres, my father was in no mood to take 'no' for an answer. So, he kept hammering, in

French – that his office had sent a telex, and received a confirmation! Notwithstanding, like a broken record, the Bulgarian kept repeating:

'Pas de réservation.'

After half an hour of this merry-go-round, in a language mixture of French, Bulgarian and Turkish, my father finally realised that he was beating a dead horse. So, albeit begrudgingly, he agreed to be directed to another hotel. However, the fact that, my mother had been threatening to go to the airport and take the first available flight back to Istanbul, might have something to do with this capitulation.

Be that as it may, the receptionist finally made a telephone call and, after some horse trading in Bulgarian, an alternative accommodation was secured. Indeed, gesticulating with his five fingers wide open, the receptionist described our new hotel:

'Cinq étoiles!'

The five-star 'Sofia Palace' turned out to be nothing short of a fleabag – no running hot water, no towels, and a room with two broken beds with covers which I would not want to venture a guess as to when they were last laundered. Seeking a scapegoat, my father announced:

'Welcome to Workers' Paradise of Comrade Stalin.'

The next morning, after breakfast, comprised of yogurt and honey, we were back on the road.

Yugoslavia was just one long bland motorway. However, it at least gave my father a chance to put his new Citroën DS to the test. As he put down his foot, the needle on the speedometer easily hit the 100 km/ph mark. Quite chuffed about his new toy, he remarked,

'This is what I call an automobile.'

By the time we finally walked through the doors of the sumptuous Hotel Imperial on Kärntner Ring, in Vienna, it was almost evening.

We had made it! Finally we were in the city of Mozart, Schubert, Beethoven and, above all, of Johann Strauss and his fabulous waltzes.

With its hand-carved statues, ornate marble, walls cocooned in silk and the massive chandeliers, Hotel Imperial exhibited all the 19th century Viennese splendour. Indeed, even my mother looked impressed.

'Khrushchev and Kennedy stayed here', my father remarked casually, 'only a few weeks ago...'

We were welcomed most courteously, the receptionist announcing they had reserved for us one of their best suites, and a single room 'für der Junge' – that is, myself. Evidently referring to our experience in Sofia, my mother observed,

'That's more like it.'

It was also at that point that the receptionist handed my father a small envelope:

'Telegraph for you.'

Obviously, thinking of his office, my father remarked:

'They can't manage even two days without me...'

However, as soon as he read the contents of the cable, his face dropped. My mother asked,

'Not good news?'

'Seems, my son is joining us.'

At this point, for the benefit of those who may be confused, I should explain, my father had been married before – to a primary school-teacher. However, as he became successful in business, he divorced the schoolteacher, and married my mother – fourteen years his junior, and a member of the Ottoman Aristocracy. Anyway, the issue of the first marriage was my half-brother, now a first-year architecture student in Venice, about to put in a surprise appearance in Vienna.

'He's arriving tomorrow.'

My father explained, trying to put a brave face to it.

Our first evening in Vienna was spent with my father looking for a restaurant he had been to before the war. Only, with his proverbial 'money does not grow on trees', he insisted that, instead of taking a taxi, we walked – as the place was 'just round the corner'.

After some forty-five minutes of scouting, as the said establishment still eluded us, I allowed myself to speak out.

'Maybe it was bombed during the war?'

'Don't talk nonsense!'

On the other hand, in her stiletto heels – hardly designed for such long hauls, my mother did not feel restricted by such rules. Taking off her shoes, she declared:

'I'm going back to the hotel, even I have to walk barefoot!'

Luckily, as we turned a corner, marked Stiftgasse, my father cried out:

'There it is! I told you so!'

Franz Joseph Hall was an elegant establishment, with waiters in white tie and live music – violins and all, playing selections from Die Fledermaus.

Our mood restored, now we were happily sampling Austrian specialities – goose liver pâté, Wiener schnitzel, washed down with vintage Mosel – of which I was allowed to have a soupçon, seeing we were in Vienna.

Indeed all seem to be going well until, evidently having decided it was 'payback time' for the forty-five minute walk, my mother remarked,

'You must be pleased, your son with that woman is joining us.'

After that, a chilly atmosphere reigned at the table. As we continued our dinner in silence, this might be a good moment to tell you a little bit about my brother.

Seven years my senior, my half-brother was a good-looking boy, blond – a rarity in Turkey, with an affable personality, equally a rare

135

quality – given, those days, most Turkish youngsters cultivated the 'macho' image, such as John Wayne, whom they frequently watched on the silver screen, in Hollywood Westerns.

Inevitably, my brother's good looks, coupled with his gentle personality, made him extremely popular with the opposite sex. Indeed, on the odd occasions he stayed with us, the phone never stopped ringing, with girls asking for a date – a phenomenon which used to turn me green with envy.

Still, beyond those rare weekends, I had little contact with him given, as soon as he completed his secondary education at the famous Lycée Galatasaray in Istanbul, he was dispatched to Venice to study architecture.

However, if truth be told, architecture was not the subject he was interested either. In fact, as a talented artist, what he really wished was to get into Beaux-Arts in Paris, and study Arts. Naturally, my father soon poured cold water onto that dream, informing him, he had no money to waste on 'airy-fairy' subjects: if he wanted to study abroad, he had better choose a 'commercially viable' field. So, that was how a compromise was reached, and my brother ended up at the Academia in Venice, studying architecture.

To revert to our story, the next day we set out to visit the Schönbrunn Palace – the summer residence of the Habsburgs, where Emperor Franz Joseph was born, and spent most of his life. Built at the end of seventeenth century, it was a truly magnificent edifice. After a quick lunch on the grounds of the palace, we returned to our hotel – where a surprise awaited us.

In the lobby of Hotel Imperial, with its grand chandeliers and walls cocooned in silk, seated on a elegant chaise longue, was my brother, chatting with a young and slender blond. My mother asked,

'Wasn't he supposed to arrive in the evening?'

'And already courting the ladies...' My father added, trying to make light of the fact this was yet another departure from an agreed plan.

'Welcome to Vienna, son.'

'Hello Dad, this is Maria...'

Now the second shoe dropped. Realising, the alluring blond was not just another tourist at the lobby of Hotel Imperial, my father's expression registered major unease. However, promptly regaining his composure, he greeted the mysterious blond:

'Très heureux.'

Maria replied also in French, with a thick Italian accent,

'Ravie de vous connaître, enfin...'

It was that 'finally', at the end of 'happy to meet you' which, I noticed, made my father hear alarm bells.

At that point, my eye also caught the bemused expression on my mother's face, observing the proceedings with studied detachment. Noticing the same, my father was quick on the uptake, introducing her:

'Ma femme...'

'Enchantée Madam.'

There was something vain, almost defiant, about Maria. I assumed, this was due to the fact she knew how sensuous and alluring she looked.

'We were not expecting you until the evening', said my father.

As my brother was about to respond, Maria butted in,

'We did not have a first-class seat on the flight so instead, Alitalia put us on a flight this morning.'

In the evening, over the welcoming dinner at another old Viennese restaurant, with the zither treating us to the strains of 'The Third Man', we got acquainted with Maria. It turned out, she was a fellow first-year Architecture student at the Accademia in Venice. My brother whispered in Turkish,

'Her father works at the Vatican.'

The next couple of days were spent, with my brother and Maria in tow, visiting the usual tourist attractions: the famous Café Sacher – the haunt of countless intellectuals and artists – Gustav Klimt, Sigmund Freud, Marlene Dietrich, Gustav Mahler, Stefan Zweig, highlighted where we sampled the renowned Sacher Apfelstrudel. Then, onto Prater – the giant ferris wheel where Orson Welles makes his famous 'Cuckoo clock speech', in the movie 'The Third Man'. Finally, a trip along the Danube, listening to voluptuous strains of 'An der schönen blauen Donau', performed by a string ensemble, on the ferry.

However, this Viennese Gemütlichkeit was frequently interrupted by some secretive activity my father and brother were engaged in – always at a quiet corner, and in hushed tones. More to the point, the conversation stopped abruptly, the moment I got anywhere near them. As this cloak and dagger play continued, I finally asked my mother:

'Why all the secrecy?'

Not without relish, my mother replied,

'She is pregnant.'

Now everything made sense: the telegraph that awaited us at the Imperial, the unscheduled arrival in Vienna, the appearance of the alluring blond and, of course, the furtive exchanges. However, on that latter item, there were still some unanswered questions: what, for example, was the purpose of those altercations?

I did not have to wait long for the answer. As usual, the consummate Mata Hari, my mother, gave me the lowdown. Maria was pregnant all right, but what was my brother going to do about it?

It transpired, while my father was turning the screws on my brother to have it 'seen to', there was, a small detail he had overlooked: Maria was a devout Catholic.

There were other complications. One should remember this was 1962 and, unlike today, when abortion is no more a morally debatable issue than a tooth extraction; those days, it was illegal – namely, a crime.

Notwithstanding, my mother reported, as far as my father was concerned, none of the aforementioned obstacles – moral or legal, did amount to a hill of beans. As usual, once he had set his mind on something, nothing could make my father change course. 'In this life, you have to be stubborn', was his favourite motto.

Consequently, I was told, a phone call was made to Zurich, where my father kept his secret bank account, and he had a chat with a certain Herr Gmünnder. Within the hour, Herr Gmünnder had called back, giving the name and address of a 'private clinic' with guaranteed discretion. My father passed this information to my brother, adding, he would, naturally, be happy to pay for the medical bills and other expenses.

However, my brother seems to have declined the offer, explaining, if he broached the subject – abortion, Maria was sure to take a walk; whereas, he was quite 'stuck on her'.

'So, what do you expect me to do!' my father seems to have roared.

'Finance you and your floozy, plus the baby, for the next five years!'

At the Accademia di Venezia, the master's degree programme in Architecture was five years.

In spite of these frank exchanges behind closed doors, when we were out and about, 'en famille', my father was perfectly courteous towards Maria, as on the day we decided to go and see a movie, to give a break to Viennese gemütlichkeit.

At this point I should casually mention that in those days, Hollywood movies reached Turkey, at least, with a three-year delay, after they had gone into distribution in Europe. Consequently, back

139

home, talking about cinema, to say that one had already seen this or that movie in Paris, London or even in Vienna, had a certain 'cachet'. That is why, I imagine, my mother suggested, that evening, we all went see 'West Side Story', a new movie which had just won ten Oscars.

'Everyone is talking about it', she exclaimed.

Although not a movie buff by any stretch of imagination, but thinking some entertainment might take his mind off the mess created by his wayward son, my father happily seconded the motion.

The concierge at the Imperial procured us tickets for the evening performance, and booked us a table at the Wienerwald at 9 pm, for dinner.

At the cinema, as the lights were being dimmed, I could see the relief on my father's face about not having to indulge in small talk with my brother's Italian sweetheart, at least for the next couple of hours.

'West Side Story' was undeniably a superb movie, with extraordinary music by Leonard Bernstein – full of syncopated rhythms which lent themselves perfectly to dance sequences. As for the plot, I soon realised the movie was a rehash of William Shakespeare's 'Romeo and Juliet', transposed to rivalry between street gangs in New York – white American 'Jets' and Puerto Rican 'Sharks'. The dramatic conflict was triggered by a member of 'Jets' falling in love with a Puerto Rican girl, played by a stunning Natalie Wood, whose brother was the leader of the Sharks.

Everything was going swimmingly as we were all immersed in the movie, enjoying the singing and dancing, until the moment young Tony who had fallen for Natalie Wood, love at first sight, decided to express his feelings in song:

'Maria… Maria… I just met a girl called Maria…'

The refrain continued, repeating the 'tritone' chord, like a gramophone record, with the needle stuck at a certain point:

'Maria... Maria... Maria... Maria...'

It was at that precise moment, my father sprung to his feet and, stepping on countless toes in the dark, swiftly headed for the 'Ausgang' sign, lit in red. Although, totally engrossed in the film, out of respect, we all had to follow suit and leave the cinema with him. Needless to say, we did not make it to the Wienerwald either. So, skipping dinner, we all ended up at the Imperial, having to content ourselves with sandwiches from the room service.

The next morning, like a general ordering retreat after the failed Siege of Vienna, my father announced we were returning to Istanbul – as of immediate effect. However, my mother declared she could not face the same punishing car journey, 'sampling the fleabags of workers' paradise!'

'Thank you, but no thank you', she concluded.

Consequently, a first-class ticket was promptly procured on the Austrian Airlines by the concierge, for her to fly back to Istanbul.

As for my brother and Maria, they too left Vienna in the morning. Indeed, they travelled to the airport in the same limousine, with my mother. Oddly, as Maria was about to get into the car, suddenly she turned around, rushed towards me and gave me a kiss, while whispering into my ear,

'Ciao Bello...'

With that, she vanished into the limousine, laid on with the compliments of the Hotel Imperial. However, as the car dwindled into the distance, it still was not clear if Maria and my brother were heading for Venice or Zurich.

Naturally, I stayed behind with my father, in order to keep him company on the return trip to Istanbul in his new Citroën DS – the very reason for the celebratory trip to Vienna.

After a few days, having gone through the same trials and tribulations of driving through the Balkans, we were finally back in Istanbul.

My mother, having arrived there a few days earlier, had already settled into her daily routine – hairdresser appointments, shopping sprees, and coffee mornings with her friends – telling them all about the latest Hollywood movie she had seen in Vienna, starring the stunning newcomer, Natalie Wood.

As for myself, now back at school, I was hugely relieved to find myself among people of my own age group, away from complicated lives of adults.

Finally, with my father back at work, life in Istanbul seemed to have settled back into its old routine – until some weeks later, when my mother had a news flash: my brother and Maria had just got married in Venice. However, she stressed, she was parting this information 'in the strictest confidence' – thus making sure I could not resist the temptation to spill the beans sooner or later.

In the event, I spilled them much sooner than anticipated. Indeed, the very same evening, at the dinner table, I casually mentioned,

'My brother and Maria seem to have tied the knot, will there be a wedding party?

Realising fully the source of the leak, my father gave an irate look at my mother, now observing the proceedings with glee. He then turned on me:

'Leave the table – NOW!'

Couple of days later he announced he was selling the Citroën DS. When I asked why, he replied,

'It… displeases me.'

HALUK

Even in his mid-teens Haluk was quite plump, a fact which prompted other kids in our class to nickname him 'piglet'. Situated at Nişantaşi, the posh neighbourhood of 1960s Istanbul, our school was an exclusive establishment, catering to the sons and daughters of well-to-do, middle-class, families.

However, Haluk was an exception. Unlike most of us whose parents were in commerce, trade or banking – that is, actively engaged in making money, Haluk's father was a landowner. In fact, that too became a subject of derision. Although owning thousands of acres, the fact that Haluk's father was a farmer, had landed him yet with another tag: 'peasant'.

So, in the Petit Bourgeois world of our school, Haluk was an 'outsider' and that is why, I imagine, we became chums. For, although my father too was a typical specimen of the middle class, income-wise, he was nowhere near some of the 'Nouveau Riche' families of the kids at school. Dad was a well-to-do broker who made a comfortable living – but no more.

Oddly, the kids at our school knew exactly what everybody's father did for a living, and their net worth. There was the son of the ship-owners, the owner of a textiles concern, somebody who works in pharmaceuticals or the such and such banking family...

Of course, at a co-ed establishment, this kind of readily available information meant the girls knew who to favour and whom to avoid. Consequently, boys from mega-rich families never had any problems with dating. Whereas my love life, such as one could have at 16, consisted purely of window shopping. My dating attempts, however elaborate, would invariably be turned down with the flimsiest of excuses.

So, that is how I, with a well-born father with no real money, and Haluk with lots of money but 'no breeding', ended up as chums. Still, he was a good sort. He rarely saw any evil in anyone, and took everything at face value. If you told him the Martians had landed in the middle of Istanbul, he would ask, 'which hotel are they staying in?'

Naturally, academically, Haluk was no Wunderkind either. Although, this was partly due to his innate laziness, in general, books simply did not interest him. Whereas, girls did. Although, those always were one-sided affairs due to his plump appearance and his 'peasant' background. Haluk's dating experience, like mine, consisted purely of star gazing.

All the same, Haluk always dressed meticulously. His blazer and trousers immaculately pressed, and his bleached shirts whiter than white, his shoes shining like mirrors, he always looked as if he was about to go on a catwalk. Perhaps, if he were not overweight, peasant or no peasant, he might even have had some success with girls... But, as things stood, he had to content himself to 'window shopping'.

Inevitably, one day, fate willed that our paths parted. During a summer holiday, in 1963, I was sent to England to learn English, and never returned. Haluk remained in Istanbul.

* * *

However, this was not to be forever. By the time I was in my third year at UCL, one evening, totally out of the blue, I got a call from Haluk. He was in London – with his wife!

When, the next day, I caught up with him, at an ostentatious rented flat on Sloane Street, I was in for another surprise. When he told me the name of his wife I almost died. She was the first girl, back in Istanbul, I had had a mad crush on; except, realising I did not stand a chance in hell, I had not even tried.

Her name was Selin. She had an expressive face with big green eyes, and red hair running down to her shoulders. She was educated at Le Rosey, an exclusive school on the shores of Lake Geneva, whose alumni included King Baudouin of Belgium, the Aga Khan, Shah of Iran and kids of countless Hollywood stars. Naturally, Selin spoke fluent French, and Turkish – with a heavy French accent. I had never come across anyone like her in Turkey.

I first met her during her summer vacation, when she was visiting her parents in Istanbul. Selin's father was the Turkish representative of a Swiss pharmaceutical company. Rumour had it, he had made his fortune, during the war, by selling penicillin in the black market. At any rate, during that fateful summer, when I met Selin at the beach residence of Cercle d'Orient, my father's club, it was love at first sight. Thinking of her, for many nights I could not sleep a wink. Mercifully, soon, I was sent to England and that was that…

After having lost contact for so many years, Haluk was genuinely pleased to see me. He had put on some more weight, but now that he was in his mid-twenties, it did not look so out of place.

As ever, he was immaculately dressed – only this time in designer labels. Slightly showing off, he gave me a guided tour: blazer from Armani, shirt from Versace, tie from Pucci, shoes from Gucci, his watch, a Vacheron Constantin which showed the time simultaneously in Istanbul, St. Moritz and London. He also wore a strong after shave, Eau Sauvage Special Edition, made exclusively, by Christian Dior, for Harrods.

'They only produce 100 bottles, every two years', he added, in his usual naivety.

I did not ask how he managed to bag a trophy such as Selin, but Haluk volunteered the information.

'It was destiny, meant to happen…'

It would appear, one day at a dinner party in Istanbul, by accident, he poured some red wine on her dress. The next day, to redeem himself, he sent her a retro emerald and diamond necklace.

'The rest is history', he concluded.

As we were chatting, his young bride arrived with as many shopping bags as her two hands could carry – Mary Quant, Oscar de la Renta, Jean Muir, Vivienne Westwood Westwood. She was wearing a huge pair of sunglasses, like Audrey Hepburn in 'Breakfast at Tiffany's', which covered most of her face.

'Salut les Copains',

Greeting me, as if last time we saw each other was a few hours ago.

After some polite chit-chat, hearing I had already been in London for a number of years, she asked if I could help them find a 'suitable' property to buy. When I asked if this meant they intended to spend some time in London, with a mysterious look, she answered,

'Qui sait…'

'What sort of thing did you have in mind?', I asked Haluk, hinting at a budget. Realising where I was coming from, he replied casually,

'Don't worry about that. I just want Selin to be happy.'

So, before long, the newlyweds moved into a duplex in Eaton Square – an exclusive neighbourhood of London.

'It's the first property the agent showed us' said Selin.

'She liked it so much, we didn't bother to look any further', added Haluk.

Obviously, he had paid the asking prize, without negotiating.

Soon enough, they settled into a routine. Their days consisted of furnishing their new duplex – choosing fabrics, wallpaper, carpets, furniture, lamps, accessories… The only problem they seem to have in their lives was to decide which restaurant to dine at, in the evening. However, the choice invariably turned out to be San Lorenzo's on Beauchamp Place – those days where the 'in crowd', such as Richard Burton, Liz Taylor, Elton John, Dustin Hoffman etc. dined.

During the day, occasionally, I accompanied Haluk and his bride, visiting Colefax & Fowler, Sanderson's and other designers on Fulham Road, while she was trying to furnish their duplex in Eaton Square. I used to find it fascinating how quickly she made her mind up. Once she liked something, it was hers. Given Haluk did not speak a word of English, nor did he make the slightest effort to learn, he literally had no say in the matter.

'I have no talent for languages, I leave that to Selin', he used to mitigate.

She, of course, spoke fluent French, and reasonable English which, either by accident or design, was laced with a strong French accent. When asked if she was French, with a mysterious smile, she would reply,

'Qui sait…'

So, before you knew it, the day was gone, and, once more, it was time to debate where to dine.

I must admit, Haluk was a generous host. His table was always full of friends – other Turks, passing through London. It always puzzled me, how all these people kept track of each other's movements, while travelling. But, through the bush telegraph, somehow they did. So, Haluk's table frequently consisted of a dozen guests, or more. Sometimes, friends turned up when we were into our desserts, apologising their flight from Paris, Geneva or Rome had been delayed. Of course, instead of catching up with others by skipping starters, they would invariably start from scratch and have a three-course meal, which meant, Haluk's table would go on ordering well past midnight.

Naturally, San Lorenzo's did not mind this in the slightest. In fact, they would often keep their kitchen going until the wee hours. Besides, the wines Haluk ordered made him a most desirable customer. Although, the suggestion came by the Sommelier – Château Lynch-Bages, Château Haut-Brion or Gevrey Chambertin, Haluk invariably followed the advice he was offered.

Besides, Haluk used to find it quite difficult to get his tongue around Chateaux Margot, Gevrey Chambertin or Château Lynch-Bages. Consequently the Sommeliers would simply ask,

'The usual?'

With a nod from Haluk, bottles of the 'usual', Gevrey Chambertin, Château Lynch-Bages, Château Haut-Brion, would be wheeled in.

Naturally, all this wining and dining had to be funded. Given those days, credit cards were not in common use, Haluk had to carry, on his person, copious amounts of hard cash, often in various currencies – Pounds Sterling, Dollars, German Marks or Swiss Francs. I later discovered, this was also due to the method used to 'transfer' the funds from Istanbul to London.

Given, in 1960s, Turkey exercised the strictest foreign exchange controls, sending money abroad was officially forbidden, indeed a criminal offence punishable with prison sentences. Consequently, all such foreign transfers had to be transacted by underhand means. In practical terms, it meant using families in Istanbul who owned multiple doner kebab joints, or 'saunas' in London… The operation was simple. In Istanbul, an employee of Haluk would hand the cash to an individual with a relative working in London; and, the next day, the equivalent of the said sum in pounds Sterling would be handed over to Haluk in Wood Green, or Stoke Newington where expat Turks operated their businesses.

Also, given the speed with which he disposed of the money, it was hardly worth banking it. Therefore, frequently, a similar operation had to be carried out also via Germany where there was a huge 'Gastarbeiter' population; and their earnings were just about enough to fund Haluk's lifestyle in London. That was the reason why Haluk always carried cash in different currencies. Given the speed with which Haluk spent the money, it was hardly worth banking the money.

Then, purely by chance, I discovered another unsavoury fact. One day, I paid an unscheduled visit to the duplex at Eaton Square, and found Haluk talking on the phone, engaged in a heated discussion. By the drift of the conversation, I gathered, he was trying to borrow money – quite a large sum at that. Moreover, he seemed to be in a desperate hurry, as he kept repeating he needed the cash '*now*'. When I asked him about it, he responded:

'Don't worry about it.'

However, given he was a school friend, I pressed him on the matter.

'If I tell you, will you promise you won't lecture?'

'I promise.'

'I lost a bit too much last night.'

Then, everything became clear. Along with his high-maintenance bride, furnishing a duplex, and subsidising various restaurateurs in London, now Haluk was gambling. So, the night before he had lost a colossal sum at the roulette table, and he had written a cheque – with no money in the bank to cover it.

'Why do you gamble?', I asked.

'Selin loves the thrill.'

Now, he was a member at the Playboy Club, Crockfords, and the

Sporting Club and was haemorrhaging at great speed. Then, with a wink, he said,

'Still, I've got a plan.'

For one moment, I thought he had discovered a system to beat the bank. Sadly, this was not the case.

'I am selling the two blocks in Taksim Square'

This was prime property in Istanbul. Noticing my nonplussed expression, he added,

'Since Dad passed away, I've got a Power of Attorney from my sisters to run the business as I see fit.' I wanted to ask,

'And… this is how you see fit?'

However, I remembered, I had promised not to 'lecture'. Besides, I had heard enough. Hoping Haluk's marriage to Selin would come to an end sooner than his money would run out, I left.

Of course this was wishful thinking. The truth was, in addition to the thousands of acres in the country, Haluk's family also owned many blocks of flats in Istanbul – all in prime locations. So, given Le Rosey educated Selin was not the type to walk away before she cleaned up all there was, this was going to be a long haul for Haluk.

Mercifully, by October, I was back at university and I lost touch with them. Some months later, I heard Selin had got bored in London, and they moved to Geneva – where she felt 'at home'.

After that, for a long while, I had no news of them. Probably subconsciously, I even forgot they existed.

* * *

Then, one New Year's Day, on January 1st, about midday, my doorbell rang. Since, I had spent the previous night at a shindig, putting out copious amounts of alcohol, I almost did not answer. However, the ringing was so persistent that, giving into a premonition, I finally caved in.

150

I was not far off the mark. There was Haluk, right before my very eyes, standing outside my door, in Cadogan Square. It was raining cats and dogs, and he had no umbrella or a raincoat. He was soaked.

Apart from the plastic carrier bag he had in his hand, from the duty-free shop at Geneva airport, he did not seem to have any luggage. Taking out a magnum of Dom Pérignon from the plastic bag, he said,

'Happy New Year.'

He looked dishevelled and tired. As we were climbing up the stairs, he explained,

'Just flew in from Geneva.'

'Where is your luggage?' My question did not seem to register.

'I knew we should never have gone to Geneva…' he mumbled.

When we entered my flat, I suggested he dried his hair, took his jacket off and put on one of my jumpers. Then, I made some coffee.

'You wouldn't have some brandy, would you?'

As I poured us two large helpings of Hine, he started talking.

This was the story: Haluk and Selin had invited a large group of friends to Club 58, a trendy night club in Geneva, to see in the New Year.

There, Selin ran into an old friend from Le Rosey, a tall, dark and handsome Argentinian, an heir to a mining fortune.

'You see, in London we were on equal footing, but in Geneva, she started playing on her own turf', Haluk murmured, in a haze…

Selin, it would appear, danced the night out with the Argentinian, even when the clock was striking midnight.

'Everyone was kissing their partners, and where was Selin?', Haluk huffed,

'On the dance floor with Speedy Gonzales, schmoozing!'

As he gulped another glass of brandy, he continued. It would appear, in the wee hours, Selin finally returned to their table – all flushed, and Haluk confronted her. She simply laughed it off:

'Don't be so Turkish!'

The rest of their exchanges basically consisted of mutual mud throwing. Finally, the whole thing peaked with Selin springing up and demanding Haluk apologise to the Argentinean.

'That's when I paid the bill and left.' Haluk concluded.

'Cheaper for the price', I said, trying to comfort him.

It would appear, thereafter, Haluk went back to their new villa, on the shores of Lake Geneva, picked up his passport and made straight for the airport from where he took the first flight to London.

'There were only three passengers on the flight' he said, concluding his story.

Given this was hardly the time to say 'told you so', I simply asked,

'Does she know you're here?'

'I left a note.'

'Why don't you just go to bed and get some sleep?'

Mercifully, Haluk did not resist. I showed him to the spare bedroom and gave him some blankets.

While Haluk was sleeping, I took stock of the situation. Obviously, God had taken pity on him and sent Speedy Gonzales to Geneva. This was the best thing that happened to him in a long time.

The danger was, when he woke up, 'forgiving her', he might want to take the first flight back to Geneva. I had to have a plan to stop him from committing such a folly.

However, in this life, on rare occasions, Destiny takes a hand; and what happened next was one of those moments: While Haluk was still asleep, my doorbell rang. It was a special delivery from Swissair. The man gave me a form to sign and handed over a suitcase. When I looked at the sender's name, sure enough, it was Selin's. She had sent Haluk's belongings – all in one single suitcase. Clearly, the Argentinian was her next catch.

Finally, having slept non-stop almost for 24 hours, Haluk surfaced. As he entered the sitting room, his eyes caught the suitcase on the floor.

'Funny, I have one just like that' he mumbled, half asleep.

'It *is* yours'

'How did it get here?'

'It arrived by Swissair cargo.'

As soon as Haluk opened the suitcase his expression changed. As he went through the contents – his shirts, ties, trousers, underwear, all squeezed and crushed on top of each other, the message became crystal clear. It was over.

A few days later, in spite of my insistence – that he was welcome to stay as long as he wished, Haluk left for Istanbul, to my relief, in order to instigate divorce proceedings.

'A duplex in London, a villa in Geneva three blocks of flats in Istanbul... A poor investment for nineteen months of marriage...' he mused, as he took his leave.

Sadly, he did not even have the pleasure of being the one to instigate divorce proceedings. By the time he arrived at Istanbul and consulted his lawyer, he was told, Selin had already got the ball rolling – on account of 'desertion'.

* * *

After that, I have not seen Haluk for quite a few years. Still, through the grapevine, I kept hearing of his news.

After divorcing Selin, on the rebound, he had married a Miss Turkey, who was also running an Escort Agency. That was followed by a German 'model'. Rumour had it, she slept with half of Istanbul and everybody knew about it – naturally, except Haluk. After the German, Haluk took an unexpected turn, seemingly for the better, once more going for respectability: namely, he started dating a RADA trained, Turkish actress, half his age. To help her career, Haluk even funded a film with her in the starring role. Only, as soon as the film was released, she took a walk. Notwithstanding, the actress was swiftly replaced by a striptease artist with a visiting dance troupe from Thailand. She became Haluk's fourth wife.

By then, after so many freeloaders and divorce settlements, not surprisingly, Haluk had fallen on hard times. Rumours abounded about him trying to borrow money from his once loyal friends on whom, in happier days, he had lavished most expensive gifts. Now, nobody wanted to know.

Surprisingly, the Thai striptease artist turned out to be the most decent of all of Haluk's women. Realising he was flat broke, she got herself a job as a receptionist at a Chinese restaurant in Istanbul and became the breadwinner of the family.

* * *

Fate wanted our paths crossed once more. One gloomy November day in London my phone rang, and the voice at the other end said,

'Guess who?'

I did not need to, I would recognise that voice anywhere. For a man, Haluk had quite a high-pitched voice, almost bordering on castrato. After the preliminaries, he asked,

'Dinner this evening?'

Thinking of his financial problems, I replied,

'Only if I invite you', adding, 'Somewhere cheap and cheerful.'

'I have no intention of having food poisoning!', he replied.

So, for old times' sake, I booked a table at San Lorenzo's.

This time, Haluk had his younger sister with him. The purpose of their visit, he explained, was to take her to a Harley Street specialist, as she was suffering with some skin disorder.

'For a woman it is important', he added.

Then he took out a thermometer from his pocket and placed it in *his* mouth. Seeing my surprise, he added,

'It's nothing.'

I did not press him on the subject, assuming he probably had a cold. The rest of the dinner at San Lorenzo's was spent with polite chit-chat.

For a couple of days I did not hear from them. On the third day I received another call. Trying to sound casual, Haluk asked if I knew a 'good doctor'.

'Is it your sister?'

'My temperature isn't going down', he replied.

Then, I remembered the thermometer at San Lorenzo's.

On the same afternoon, we ended up at my GP, on Basil Street. As we were waiting our turn, I assured Haluk, the man he was about to see was one of the top physicians in London, who, among his patients counted Mrs Thatcher the present prime minister. When it was Haluk's turn to go in, he said,

'Please come in with me.'

I certainly was not prepared for that, nor for what took place thereafter. As we settled at the doctor's surgery, and I explained Haluk was a childhood friend of mine, there came the proverbial question:

'What seems to be the trouble?'

Haluk replied, he had cancer – Non-Hodgkin lymphoma, adding, 'But now I'm cured.'

'So why are you here?' asked the doctor.

Haluk explained, for the last few days he had temperature, about 38°C. The doctor took Haluk's temperature and informed him,

'Actually, it's 39°C.'

Then he moved on to explain: Non-Hodgkin lymphoma was a serious form of Cancer, and Haluk's high temperature indicated, he should be hospitalised immediately.

'I could arrange it right now.'

Haluk was in no mood to listen. He replied, he had a 'great specialist' in Turkey – the very best, and he had complete trust in him.

'If he says I have no cancer, it means I have no cancer' adding he probably had picked up a cold.

The rest of the consultation was spent with Haluk wanting to have some medication to simply reduce his temperature, and the doctor, tactfully, trying to hammer into him that he ought to check into a hospital now. All that fell onto deaf ears. As we were leaving, the doctor whispered into my ear,

'There's not a moment to lose.'

In the cab, given I knew he was flat broke, I offered to pay Haluk for his medical expenses, if he checked into a hospital immediately. He replied,

'Mrs Thatcher's doctor – a businessman, what do you expect?'

The next day, Haluk took his sister to Harley Street, to see the dermatologist. They stayed on in London for another week, waiting for the results of the tests they had done on her. Then, they finally flew back to Istanbul. Haluk died three days later.

I heard the news from his sister, who called me from Istanbul. Crying on the phone, she sighed,

'Just as well. We had sold the last of family heirlooms. There is nothing else left to sell.'

* * *

On reflection, I still wonder what really attracted all these women to Haluk. I know it is easy to say it was the money, but was it?

To this day, I believe there was something else about him, which appealed to women. Still, whatever the secret was, he took it with him to his grave. So now, we will never know. Except, I am absolutely certain, it was not only the money.

XANADU

Like most ventures, this one too started with a phone call. As I lived in London, it was a long distance – from Istanbul. On the other end of the line was a friend of mine, from a well-known, well-to-do family, as his father was the founder of the biggest bank in Turkey. The gist of it was, there was a recently built film studio in Antalya, on the Mediterranean shores of Turkey, and its owner, a billionaire industrialist, wanted to sell it. So, with my contacts in the film industry, could I find a buyer?

At this point, perhaps, I should say a few words about myself. Although Turkish, I had been living in London since my late teens, by then almost thirty years, and recently had produced a film which enjoyed a Royal Première. Hence the request for me to act as an estate agent to sell the said property, the asking price for which was a neat fifty million dollars – those days a small fortune! Needless to say, if I were to succeed in the said enterprise, my commission, albeit a minute percentage, would amount to a serious sum. Naturally, I answered:

'Would be delighted, if I could be of help…'

The fact that I had not got the faintest idea how one sold a film studio, hardly came into the equation.

'Good, I'll fax you the details', said my friend, adding:

'By the way, the owner wants a quick sale.'

When I asked why, I got a curt answer:

'Private reasons.'

The tone in my friend's response left me in no doubt as to I was not to ask any further questions on this matter.

Although an affable fellow, like most of his ilk, 'second generation money' – as in, he did not have to work for it; when it came to having a rational conversation, my friend always had a short fuse. Be that as it may, in his time, he was very much a part of the 'Jet Set'. Starting life at an exclusive international school in St. Moritz, Switzerland, later, thanks to the 'good offices' of the British ambassador to Turkey, he had ended up at Trinity College, Cambridge University. Only, one day he was summoned to the Dean's office who reminded him undergraduates were not allowed to have a car. My friend protested:

'But, I do not have a car.'

'That's not what I hear'.

'I have two.'

Upon which, without further ado, my friend was sent down, putting an abrupt end to his days at Cambridge University. Mind you, just as well. For, although excelling in sports, such as kresta riding and skiing on the slopes of St. Moritz, he was hardly the academic type… So, he returned to Istanbul and, to fill his time, he started a vintage automobile collection – comprising of a few Ferraris, Maseratis, a couple of Alfa Romeos, and a Hispano Suiza. Also, every year, he participated in the Paris-Dakar Rally.

Anyway, to revert to our story, a few minutes later, the details of the studio turned up at my fax machine – those days regarded as a miracle of twentieth-century technology. The studio consisted of two sound stages of gigantic proportions, with all the ancillary facilities – artist dressing rooms, script conference rooms; costume storage rooms; lighting & camera equipment storage areas; plus many acres of 'backlot' – for exterior shooting. In short, this was a set up fit for an MGM musical.

So, now, all I had to do was to find an obliging fellow, prepared to part with fifty million US dollars, and I could pick a up a handsome commission. Even if it were 1%, I would walk with $500,000, paid in Switzerland and tax-free! However, where was this amendable gentleman?

After countless fruitless phone calls, I realised I was hitting my head against a brick wall. I simply did not have the kind of clout to sell a property with a fifty-million-dollar price tag – in 1985 a colossal sum. On the other hand the clock was ticking. Surely, I was not going to let $500,000 slip through. I just had to try harder!

However, weeks passed, and there still was not even a glimmer of hope on the horizon. Yet, in the course of my enquiries, I discovered it was impossible to get a space in any of the London studios – Pinewood, Shepperton or Elstree; consequently American producers were now taking their films across to communist bloc countries – Yugoslavia, Bulgaria, Poland or Hungary. Surely, a state-of-the-art studio, sitting on the Mediterranean coast of capitalist Turkey, should be a piece of cake to sell. But to whom?

Finally, I had to accept the reality: I simply was not in that league. The time had come to call my friend with the collection of vintage cars, and tell him the truth: I had failed.

That evening, to drown my sorrow, I walked into the Carlton Tower bar, my local, so to speak, and ordered a double scotch. After a string of those, just as the world around me was beginning to look conveniently surreal, I heard a voice:

'Hey, what are we celebrating?'

It was Sean O'Reilly, an Irishman I knew of old, who, with his wife, ran a film sales agency in London. In case you don't know what a film sales agency does, those are the guys running up and down the Croisette during the Cannes Film Festival, with flyers in their pockets, who sell 'independent films' to distributors from various countries: 'This one's great! Terrific car chase, plenty of violence, lesbian vampire sisters, in cahoots with Dracula running a drug cartel.'

Given by now I was past caring, it did not take me long to pour out my sorrow to Sean. After a few more Johnnie Walker Black Labels, Sean said:

'Go and see Kevin Collins at Morgan Friedlander Bank. He runs the Media Department.'

'Why would he buy a film studio in Turkey for $50m?'

'Because, he's bent.' With that, O'Reilly vanished.

The next morning, as soon as my hangover cleared, I dialled the phone number Sean gave me. A posh voiced answered. I mumbled that I wished to speak with the head of the Media Department. Soon I was talking to Kevin Collins. I quickly explained the purpose of my call. By the time I finished, expecting a 'No thanks', Collins said:

'Would you care to lunch at the bank?'

The walls of the dining room of this eighteenth-century building which housed the bank were covered with oil portraits of past chairmen: Sir..., Lord... etc. Lunch passed with me pitching the studio to Collins and his colleagues. Finally, over cigars and VSOP brandy, Collins responded,

'Any chance of seeing this studio?'

As I was leaving, Collins walked me down, all the way to the entrance on Threadneedle Street. There, squeezing my arm, he whispered,

'Maybe, we could work something out... '

That evening I called Istanbul and announced the good news.

'I knew you'd pull it off!' bellowed my friend.

The only problem was logistics: those days there were no direct flights from London to Antalya. Consequently, first, one had to fly to Istanbul; then, the next day, catch the connecting flight – which meant a day and a half lost with travelling. Of course, on the way back, one had to do the reverse. Allowing one clear day to inspect the studio and talks, we needed, at least, four days. Only, Collins was not happy to absent himself from work for that length of time.

Then the penny dropped: Obviously, for the moment, Collins was embarking on this enterprise under his own steam. If things worked out, he would inform the bank. In desperation, I called back Istanbul and explained the dilemma, making out, 'due to his busy schedule', Collins was finding it difficult to clear his diary for four days.

'We have foreseen that' my friend answered, 'Mr Tokatli will send you his private jet.'

* * *

Forty-eight hours later, one early morning, I picked up Collins from his home in Hampstead Garden Suburb, and we headed for Luton airport – where Mr Tokatli's Lear jet was waiting for us. Given the car was allowed onto the tarmac, and with no passport controls, we boarded the jet straightaway. As we were taxiing for takeoff, Collins quipped,

'Only way to travel…'

The trip was fairly uneventful, except, somewhere over the Greek Islands, sipping a glass of Bollinger, Collins dropped the other shoe: 'should… the deal go through', he expected to share in the sales commission 50/50 – payable to a Swiss account.

So, in one breath, I had lost $250,000. On the other hand, given 'should the deal get through' made it crystal clear that without sharing my commission, there was no way the deal would 'go through'. So, I could look at the situation as if I just had made £250,000. My film salesman friend, Sean O'Reilly's parting words reverberated in my head: 'He's totally bent.'

As we landed at Antalya airport, I could see my friend leaning on a black Mercedes, waiting for us. After the introductions, and a perfunctory passport control on the tarmac, we were on our way to the studio. In the car, my friend spoke to me in Turkish,

'By the way, don't ever mention the word Anorexia.'

'Why would I do that' I asked, puzzled.

'Because, his daughter is anorexic.'

'Maybe they should seek advice abroad, in America...' Then came another curt answer:

'She lives in America.'

My friend apologised to Collins for speaking Turkish, and the rest of the trip was spent with polite small talk.

At the Studio, we were welcomed by Mr Tokatli himself, a man in his fifties, in a white linen suit, with thick 'Onassis' sunglasses which covered half his face. He was surrounded by numerous minions. After the introductions, addressing himself to Collins, Tokatli spoke in his heavily accented English,

'My manager will show you around, then we meet at my bureau.'

With that he disappeared, as we set out on our guided tour of the property with a $50 million price tag.

In the event, it turned out to be much more magnificent than I ever imagined. Evidently, no expense was spared to create a film studio to the highest international standards. For starters, it had two gigantic sound stages in which we, mere humans, looked like insignificant little dots. Then came the stars' dressing rooms – complete with their marble jacuzzis and private gyms. There were script conference rooms, projection theatres with Pullman seats, make-up rooms, costume storage facilities etc. As for technical stuff – with lighting equipment, spotlights of various sizes, cherry pickers, gigantic wind machines etc. nothing was left out.

Last but not least, there was the back lot for exteriors. A long stretch with various façades – a New York Street, a street in Paris complete with the Eiffel Tower in the background.

Only, an eerie silence reigned in this edifice – for, there was not a single soul to be seen anywhere.

The question was what on earth had possessed this Turkish billionaire, who made his fortune in pharmaceuticals and chemical fertilisers, to build a film studio fit to shoot any of the grand MGM musicals?

Now, as instructed, we were back at the wood-panelled executive office, where Tokatli was seated behind a mahogany desk. On it stood a large, silver framed photograph of a young and attractive woman, with an enigmatic expression. Noticing me studying the picture, as if to stop me from opening my big mouth, my friend quickly whispered into my ear,

'His daughter!'

'The anorexic?'

My friend gave me a sharp look. Luckily, examining some sketches on the wall, now Tokatli was explaining to Collins, the studio was designed by the same English firm of Architects as those who built Shepperton Studios.

'The whole thing cost me exactly $50 million dollars – I'm not making one Cent profit.'

Tokatli, was not an easy character to figure out. The fact that, even indoors, he kept his large sunglasses on, did not help either. Still, I had a strange feeling he was telling the truth. Changing gear, he then asked if the food on the flight was 'OK'.

'Caviar and champagne… we managed.' answered Collins, with a belly laugh. Then, counting on the relaxed atmosphere, he extended his comedy act:

'So, what made you want to go into show business?'

'I didn't.' was the curt response.

165

After that, we were told the driver would take us to our hotel, the Tokatli Palace, where we could freshen up. The dinner was at '8 pm sharp.' On the way to the hotel, I asked Collins,

'What do you think?'

'He wants to sell all right.' Then, he muttered:

'It just doesn't add up…'

'What?'

'Why go into all this trouble?'

* * *

Dinner was served on the terrace of this five-star hotel, overlooking the Mediterranean. Given it was not the tourist season yet, except for a few German couples, the terrace was almost empty. Notwithstanding, there was a small band playing Argentinian Tangos. By now it had got dark and the full moon was reflecting on the Mediterranean, lying at our feet.

At the top of the table was Tokatli, now in a white tuxedo with a red carnation, and still wearing his 'Onassis' sunglasses. He asked Collins to sit next to him. I was told to sit on his left, and my friend took the seat facing Tokatli.

We started with Lobster Thermidor, washed down with Cankaya Special Cuvée, an exquisite Turkish white wine. Lobster was followed by tender lamb and vegetables washed down with Chateau Margaux, 1962. After a while, taking advantage of a break in the music, raising his glass, Tokatli stood up. He thanked Collins for travelling 'all the way' to Turkey – hopefully to result in a mutually advantageous business deal.

'I propose a toast to my friend, Mr Collins.'

Now, it was Colin's turn to speak. Lifting his glass, he thanked Tokatli for his 'generous hospitality', and congratulated him on his 'extraordinary achievement'. Finally, to my relief, he ended his speech with – 'I look forward to doing business with Mr Tokatli!'

That was it! Clearly, I would be returning to London $250,000 richer. Now, springing on his feet again, and clinking his glass with Colins', Tokatli spoke,

'For a young man who arrived in Istanbul with 17 Liras in his pocket, I haven't done too badly...'

Then, something unexpected took place: suddenly losing his balance, Tokatli collapsed onto his seat. Gasping for breath, he was now trying to undo his bow tie. My friend yelled out:

'Get a doctor!'

Petrified, everyone around the table paralysed, afraid to make the slightest move. However, Tokatli somewhat managed to get a small bottle of pills out of his pocket, and swiftly shoved them in his mouth. On the terrace, one could hear a pin drop. Still, within minutes, Tokatli seem to regain his composure. Now, breathing normally,

'It's OK' he whispered, adding, 'These are magic pills...'

However, by now, the atmosphere at the table was altered for good. My friend said,

'Maybe we should leave...'

On that note, thanking him for an exquisite evening, we all got up to take our leave. It was at that moment Tokatli gently touched my arm, and whispered,

'Would you please stay.'

Noticing the commotion at our table, the musician had packed up too, as did the German couples at other tables. So now, Tokatli and I were the only people left on the terrace. For a while, we contemplated the Mediterranean, with the moon reflecting on it. Finally, Tokatli spoke.

'I know you're dying to know why I built it, and why I'm selling it.' He took a sip of wine, and continued.

'At first, I wanted to burn it down. Then I thought, what's the point, the insurance company would refund the money.'

Wondering if he was jesting, I discreetly studied him. Oddly, by now, he had removed his sunglasses, and I could see his eyes. He was damn serious. I felt, he needed to talk.

'It has always been her... Her only.'

'Cherchez la femme', I thought. Now we were getting somewhere... He continued,

'She never wanted for anything – ever. I showered her with everything... The very best... What's the point of making money, if you can't please those you love?'

'You are... married?'

'Was – was married. One day, out of the blue, she asked for a divorce.'

'A costly divorce?'

'Not a dime! She said, she simply didn't want to come between me and her.'

Now, I was confused. Who was 'her'? Then the penny dropped. How could I have been so blind! The woman Tokatli was talking about was none other than the girl in the silver framed photograph on his desk. Only... what had the film studio got to do with all this? Was Tokatli trying to make a movie star out of his anorexic daughter?

'She had a touch of... anorexia, you know.' He continued.

'I took her to the best specialists – all over Europe. No use...Then, someone recommended this Turkish specialist, a young guy, who studied in some university in America.'

Tokatli took another sip of wine.

'I knew right away he was a charlatan, He suggests this fancy clinic – in California! He says, pop stars, movie stars go there. All druggies! Is my Baby a druggie? Still, she was wasting away... What choice did I have?'

Now, things were beginning to make sense. The anorexic daughter, the clinic in California. But, why the film studio?

'Was she cured?'

'After three months, I admit, the clinic reported she was taking regular meals. She was almost ready to come home.'

'Great!'

'I even booked her flight home.'

'And?'

'And… she meets this guy, the film director.'

'No!'

'Yes! Three days before she is due to fly back home!'

'Film director?'

'The only thing he ever directed was one episode of a TV series. It was so bad, they took the whole thing off the air.'

'So?'

'So… she wouldn't come home.'

'That's terrible.' I lied, trying to sound like I was on his side.

Suddenly, Tokatli banged his fist on the table.

'You don't fuck with Tokatli. My Baby's coming home!'

So, there it was: If the daughter would not come home alone, she had to come with the boyfriend. And the studio was the fifty-million-dollar bait.

'I got the whole thing completed in less than six months – people worked after hours and weekends…'

'Miraculous' I said.

'Here's the deal: He brings my Baby back home, and he can have a film studio at his disposal. I would even finance his films – personally. But, I want my baby back, here!'

If I had not seen the studio with my own eyes, I would have sworn Tokatli was making it all up as he went along. But, it still did not add up.

'Now, you want to know why I'm selling, don't you?'

'I was hoping, the story would have a Happy End.'

'Sure they came back, and Mr Big Shot liked what he saw.'

'Then?'

'Then, my friend… one good day, they were gone. Just like that… She had left a note – on the kitchen table. It read: 'Love LA. Sorry—'

Three words! $50 million, for three words… A very poor investment indeed.'

By now, I could see the sun rising on the horizon, over the Mediterranean. Tokatli slowly got up, and left some banknotes on the table.

'Thank you for listening. Let's go.'

* * *

A few hours later, Tokatli's Lear Jet was waiting for us on the tarmac. With no one to see us off, we just had our passports stamped and boarded. Soon, we taxied along the runway and were airborne. As we climbed, through the window, I could see Tokatli's studio standing tall on the Anatolian planes.

As we were over the Greek Islands, sipping his Champagne, Collins said,

'This isn't going to work, I'm afraid.'

'Oh?'

'They have no infrastructure to run a film studio. Producers expect more than four walls. I couldn't sell the idea to the bank.'

There went my $250,000. But, somehow, I felt relieved.

'Oh well, you can't win 'em all…' I replied

Finally, you might wonder, whatever happened to the Studio. These days, I hear, it is being used as a storage facility for Tokatli's chemical fertilisers.